SAFE SPACE

SAFE SPACE

How to survive in a threatening world

ANTHONY FRY

J. M. Dent & Sons Ltd
London   Melbourne

First published 1987
© Anthony Fry 1987

Set in 10½/12½pt Ehrhardt
by Gee Graphics Ltd
Printed by Mackays of Chatham Ltd
for J. M. Dent & Sons Ltd
Aldine House, 33 Welbeck Street, London W1M 8LX

British Library Cataloguing in Publication Data

Fry, Anthony
    Safe space: how to survive in a
    threatening world.
    1. Human ecology
    I. Title
304.2   GF41

ISBN   0-460-04708-6

CONTENTS

To Lynda
and our three sons
Alexander, Nick and Robert

PREFACE

For Robert Graves, poetry was the crowning privilege and the inspiration of the Muse an essential part of the creative process, so perhaps it is to her that I should first give thanks. As other people have enjoyed dancing or painting, I have always loved the process of writing. My adolescent journals, running to thousands of pages, now lie gathering dust on the bookshelf. This book, like those dusty diaries, is inspired by my personal and professional experiences.

Much of medicine is very private and its public presentation only occurs in a variety of formalised settings. In this book part of what I have learnt from twenty years of practice, ten of them as both a teaching hospital consultant and an independent practitioner, is allowed some exposure. Thus another thanks is to Medicine, to my teachers at King's College Hospital, at the Maudsley and at the Institute of Psychiatry. Thanks also to my colleagues, students, fellow team members and patients at Guy's, with whom I work on Job Ward in New Guy's House, and at Chaucer Day Hospital at St Olave's Hospital.

In writing this book I have been well aware of my debt to much of psychiatry, both dynamic and social, and to many branches of medicine, including environmental medicine, public health, health promotion and holistic medicine, all of which have inspired me and contributed to the ideas within this book.

On a more personal level, special thanks go to my publishers who first suggested that I write this book and who, at all stages, have backed the project with enthusiasm. Similarly Annie Anderson has generously applied her journalistic expertise and fine criticism, with good humour and encouragement throughout, especially at times when I was sure a fourth draft could not improve matters.

Many old and close friends have been enthusiastic and very helpful. Thanks to Mike Lesser for his divergent approach, Mark Kidel for his ecological understanding and helpful proof reading, and Nick Mason for his fine appreciation of danger. Other friends who have helped and encouraged me include Lizzie Devenish, Liz McCormick, Michael Ginsborg, Charlie Clarke, Wendie Phillips, Lyndi Mason, Gawn Grainger and my sister Ruth Fischelis.

My mother's endless energy and enthusiasm has, as usual, been applied in the form of encouragement and faith, but also in helping me to develop what I hope is a readable and understandable style. I want also to acknowledge my great debt to my late father, whose broad and always original mind did so much to inspire my early studies and my first contact with a variety of psychoanalytic writers. I also owe so very much to the late Florence Louise Chapman.

Other friends to whom I owe thanks include Roger Crossthwaite, John Gallagher, Philip Thomas, Fiona Edwards-Stuart, Stephanie Wuensche, Sophie Johnson, Richard and Liz McKane and Jim Anderson.

I owe a special intellectual debt to John Bowlby, Rene Dubois, Desmond Morris, Fritjof Capra, Shunryu Suzuki, Erick Erickson, Felicity Huntingford and George Brown. Thanks to John Marshall, who gave me invaluable advice on motivation, to Ginnie Smith, whose wide knowledge of medical history gave important technical back-up, to Michal Power and Karen Mogg for advice on cognitive therapy and social support. Thanks also to Roland Littlewood, Joe Berke, Pamela Taylor, Don McCullin and Anthony Holden.

More indirect inspiration came from my contact with Charles Rycroft, Anthony Storr, Gillian Barnett, Andrew Watson and Wendy Ashton, all of whom have taught me a great deal.

Many colleagues at Guy's have given their time and expert advice, and these include Tom Craig, Amanda Ramirez, Angela Summerfield, Jim Watson, Elaine Murphy, Sara Nicholson, David Armstrong and Phil Timms. Other colleagues I would like to thank include John Fleminger, Maurice Lipsedge, Paul Bridges, Jill Stanford, Jill Hardman and Lilian Meakins. I would also like to thank all my editorial colleagues at *Holistic Medicine* and the British Holistic Medical Association, especially Maureen Green, whose broad literary knowledge was so often helpful.

I am very grateful to Jane Godfrey for all her help and encouragement during the early stages of the book, and my very grateful thanks go to Janet Spence, whose attention to detail, good humour (especially when the word processor broke down) and commitment have been invaluable.

I must give special thanks to my sons: to Alexander, for his fine taste in mystic stories and his readiness to run me into the ground when my brain needed to be displaced by my body; to Nicholas, for his endless supply of jokes, anecdotes and his gymnastic prowess; and to Robert, for the stories he has read to me and the boxing matches we have fought together.

Finally, my greatest thanks to my wife Lynda, who is also a wonderful friend, a witty and observant critic, and a brilliant accomplice in my pursuit of safe space, who has unselfishly encouraged me to write this book, and often, with considerable effort, found the space for me to do it.

INTRODUCTION

A major part of my medical practice is as a consultant psychiatrist at Guy's Hospital, where I treat people suffering from quite severe mental disorders. Most of the time I feel like a doctor, but on occasions I feel like a priest and at other times I feel as if I am a soldier. I have often been fascinated by these feelings, and wondered why the experience of medicine can be so very different on different occasions. That there should be a similarity between hospital practice in London and war seems unlikely and improbable and yet the link was there, and it was this in particular that really led to the development of the ideas within this book.

I began to realise that I felt like a soldier because the people with whom I was working were living in a war zone. Not that there was any new and undeclared war that the outside world had somehow omitted to notice, but quite simply the conditions that some of them had to face seemed to me to be like the conditions that one would expect in war time. Often I would go on to the ward in the early evening and it was rather like a dressing station some few miles back from the front line. There, in their beds, would be the casualties. Some were there with straightforward mental disorders, but for others the story was more complex: one had perhaps been mugged, another would have been evicted, another would have jumped out of a window, one would have run away from her violent husband, another would have just overdosed on heroin. These casualties, not unexpectedly, had a variety of psychiatric problems which included anxiety states, depression, hypochondria and a number of conditions featuring some form of persecution – often psychotic states.

These diagnoses helped us to draw up treatment plans and to deliver appropriate personal support and medical input. All this was very much needed, but often it seemed to miss the real issue and to neglect vital causative factors. I had worked in medicine in Africa and travelled in a variety of third world countries. People there, who are starving or suffering from prolonged malnutrition, parasitic infestation and have no clean drinking water, will eventually develop a variety of well-defined diseases. These easily gain a hold in a thin, frail, exhausted body. The malnutrition comes first and the disease readily follows on.

How thin and frail and exhausted were the souls and spirits of those front line patients at Guy's Hospital? What had battle zone conditions done to them? What had twenty or thirty years of general deprivation done to them? No loving family in childhood, no safe or secure home, no job, no friends – how starved were they, how would we describe their malnutrition? Week after week, year after year I and the teams with whom I worked, on the acute ward at the hospital, at the day hospital and out in the community, would see people suffering in this way with these diverse problems, yet so much was wrong in many areas of their lives that it was quite difficult to put a label to it and to begin to define it.

These casualties, although they represented only a very small fraction of the general population, became very important to me, and the more I worked with them the more clear it became to me that many of them had something quite outstanding in common. That common feature was to do with the environments in which they lived. By environment, I don't just mean whether they lived in a tower block or a cellar or a luxury flat, I don't just mean whether they had hot water or a bath or an inside lavatory. I began to realise that environment was not merely the material conditions under which they lived, but the personal links that they made with the world, whether these were intimate or social, and as well as that, the way they thought about these links and the way they felt in general about their world. If they were mentally ill or disabled, their personal environment could often make things worse. If they had not previously been ill and their personal environments became too unsettled or disrupted, they often seemed to develop mental illness. There was another group where the picture was rather more subtle – for at first it seemed as if their personal and material worlds supplied most of their basic requirements – but in the past, often in childhood, they had experienced a prolonged period of deprivation and insecurity, and now, as adults, even when in 'good enough' conditions, they were unable to appreciate them, make use of them or feel good. They had adapted to war and even in the demilitarised zone they could feel no sense of peace, no safety.

Early in 1982 I began to feel rather concerned about the way medical practice was going. Whilst I sincerely believed in the efficacy of much modern medicine, I sometimes felt that it was inappropriately applied and that often its approach was too narrow. Later on in 1982, whilst looking for some new way forward, I was fortunate to meet up with a small group of other doctors in medical practice who were exploring some new ideas. Together, as Trustees, we formed the British Holistic Medical Association and planned a launching conference for September 1983. It was agreed that I would present a paper at this and I tried to find a theme that interested me. I had always been fascinated by the doctor/patient relationship and began to work hard on trying to explore some new aspects of this.

During the summer I went with my wife to stay with very close friends at a beautiful house in the South of France. It was an old house, washed in red and covered with creepers and flowers. There were grapevines in the garden and the whole place had a feeling of safety and security about it. In the afternoons, when it was very hot, I used to sit in my room looking out over this beautiful garden and work on the paper for the forthcoming conference. One afternoon I was very much aware of the presence of the house and the feeling of security that it, and those within it, gave to me. I realised that this feeling was quite closely related to the feeling that occurs when there is a deep and trusting relationship between two human beings. There was something of this in the writings of Martin Buber and his discussion of what occurred between Man and Man.

I gave the name 'safe space' to this aspect of the medical consultation and described it in some detail in the paper that I read at the launching conference. In this paper I confined myself to the idea of safe space simply in relation to the medical consultation, suggesting that the trust, warmth and acceptance of the doctor created a 'safe space' in which the patient could reveal his or her illness and distress and share his or her problems with the doctor and, if necessary, submit to intimate physical examination. Some weeks after the conference, I was approached by the publishers of this book, who had been stimulated by my presentation and suggested I write a book about it. I was extremely busy and the idea seemed somewhat daunting, but the more I thought about it, the more fascinated I became and the more sure I was that it was very important to try to organise these ideas in some systematic way.

Late in the autumn I went on my own to work on the book in Wales. I stayed in a small house in the hills of Mid Wales. It was cold and the north wind was icy. There was no electricity and no running water. At night I worked by the light of only one oil lamp and cooked my supper on a small wood fire. Safe space was with me again – this small, dry, windproof house, the wood fire and the oil lamp were the only technology that made my immediate personal environment suitable for human habitation. In the electric centrally heated environment of the big city, it was all too easy to forget the fragility of the human form and the brutality of nature.

It was rapidly becoming clear to me that safe space could be considered in a much wider context. The old house in the South of France had provided me with safe space, just as being with close friends had also provided me with safe space. I began to realise that in safe space I had identified that quality of personal, social and material environment which was so important to us all, and so obviously missing in my front-line patients living around Guy's Hospital. The material spaces in which they lived were frequently unsafe. Not only the tower blocks and walkways and shopping centres, but the personal and social spaces in which they lived were equally unsafe. Families fell apart, jobs disappeared and there was often a pervasive distrust. People were on guard

INTRODUCTION

against a world that they had learned from childhood to suspect – a world that was unsafe.

Safe space wasn't relevant just to them, it was relevant to me, to my friends and to everybody else that I knew. Each and every one of us needed it. I began to realise quite clearly that safe space was provided not only by intimate personal contact, but by caring professional contact, by social life, by the work place, by the material world around us and by a whole series of beliefs and commitments that we have in relation to our lives. Safe space began to emerge as a broad and general survey of the personal and material environment, and in particular its role in bodily and mental function. Safe space became something created between two people and something that involved an interaction between the world outside and the way we felt within about the world outside. Even if the world outside was right, if we felt bad about it, felt unsafe and without trust within, then we would not feel safe.

As I looked carefully at this rather threatening world, it seemed that safe space for many of us was becoming increasingly hard to find and that for a whole variety of reasons, material, social and personal conditions were becoming ever more unsuitable for human beings. I am convinced that many of us feel this and know this. In this book I have tried to define a framework that gives scheme and clarity to a problem that intrudes at many levels of society in all kinds of disguises. I am convinced that as individuals we need to affirm the importance of these things for ourselves, and in a broader context for society and the world as a whole. We must clearly identify this problem, particular for our age and our time, and having identified it, we must try to set about putting things right. This book, I hope, will be a step towards doing that.

1

THE SPACE THAT WE NEED TO LIVE

In a changing world one constant element is us. In amongst the artifacts of culture, technology and social organisation, we remain soft and naked – born from the womb, eating, sleeping, loving, reproducing, building, creating and growing old. For all that we have made and thought and dreamed of and become, we have carried our basic needs with us and these make the same material and interpersonal demands that they made one hundred thousand years ago. In the vast variety of human cultures and habitats, obvious and recurrent patterns persist. Homes from mud huts to suburban houses serve very similar purposes, with central hearths for cooking and designated areas for sleeping. There are recurrent patterns of family and kinship with their taboos, loyalties and loves, and people in various cultures show common responses to birth, marriage and bereavement.

We may identify the conditions that sustain us as 'safe space'. Civilisation and culture may change, but our basic environmental requirements do not. Ironically, the very technology we have developed to provide those needs – energy, food and social structure – is all too often failing to fulfil its promise. In a polluted world, many natural cycles begin to fail. Cities and homes become ever more vulnerable and families and communities lose their stability. The hidden menace of Chernobyl lies in the soil waiting to be absorbed by the vegetables and meat that we shall eat this year and next year and for many, many years to come. The crime rates carry on rising, more and more children become victims of divorce, broken homes and abuse. Rates of mental illness, drug addiction and alcoholism go on rising. A common theme emerges – the world is becoming unsuitable for human consumption – the world is becoming unsafe.

A hundred years ago the pride of science lay in the meticulously labelled dinosaur bones carefully wired together or the stuffed ape skin with its still staring glass eyes. This was the study of static things. Now we are also interested in processes, in the way living things move and change. We are interested in systems that perform functions. Now we want to know how those dinosaurs lived, what they ate, where they laid their eggs, why they suddenly died out. Now we are interested in the reports of the investigators who have actually lived with apes – eaten with them, cuddled with them, watched how they respond to danger, how they defend their territory, how they fight and how they play.

Our understanding of ourselves and our place in the world is developing very rapidly. For a long time each department in the university or medical school marked off its piece of territory and plugged away at it, believing grandiosely that its contribution alone was the special one that would finally give the answer. Early developments in medical and biological knowledge worked well enough with bits of us and have proved very useful. Thanks to the physiologists, we have vast knowledge of the heart and how it pumps all on its own, and the stomach and how it digests all on its own. This trend to fragment phenomenon and study it in parts has, of course, dominated Western thought and science for three hundred years, and it has yielded much, but it is now running into difficulties. Scientists and investigators in a whole variety of disciplines from psychology to atomic physics seem to agree on that. New paradigms are needed in which many of the components of a phenomenon have to be included to produce a comprehensive whole.

In pursuit of the mind, the psychoanalysts took the patient out of his or her world and, in somewhat artifical and regulated conditions, they pursued and analysed the hidden recesses of the psyche, but, whilst doing this, they paid little attention to the body or the real world in which the patient lived. It is becoming clear that we cannot go on looking at the mind as if there were no body, or the body as if there were no mind. We are more than just a mind, full of conflicts or complexes or ego states. We are bodies too, arms, legs, bellies, bottoms and internal organs. We need a whole person approach that looks at mind, at body and the way they interrelate.

Having defined a whole person, we need to go further. We need to see how that whole works, in terms not only of the systems within it, but of the way the whole itself is a component in still larger systems. It takes two or more people to create a family system or unit and millions to create a city. Rather than static dead slices of matter, we need to think of living, moving, changing systems that interact and develop.

It is becoming quite clear that useful truths about us and our place in the world are going to demand broad collaborative effort across a whole range of disciplines. And as well as looking at the functioning whole, we also need to look at the world in which the whole person with mind and body actually lives, breathes, eats, and loves, along with a whole lot of other people. We need a whole person in a whole world, a living system in a safe space.

We need to emphasise the idea of an interreactive system in which we relate freely and actively with our environment. We are not passive creatures. We have faith, beliefs, goals and expectations and they profoundly affect the way we respond. A bull fighter expecting a bull, and knowing how to respond, may not experience the bull ring as a very unsafe space, whereas you or I might. We can make choices. A bull fighter may choose to enter a bull ring – you or I might not. That bull fighter has adapted to his special conditions of life (or at least we hope he has), and he is there because he chose to be there. Those elements of will, freedom, choice and challenge will vitally affect his behaviour in that ring.

We can't abstract or separate ourselves any longer from the places or spaces in which we live. We need to think not just of us, but of us functioning in relation to an environment which affects every aspect of our lives in all kinds of ways. Personal awareness of this can make a major contribution to our survival as well as to our health and general sense of well-being.

The pursuit of ideal living conditions has always been a fundamental priority for human beings. We are free. We can define and choose goals and then pursue them. Could it be that we have forgotten our basic human requirements? We need to define and identify those conditions that are suitable for human life. It is no good trusting to chance or to market forces and hoping that the right conditions emerge.

We can do much to make our lives safer by understanding the nature of the spaces we need and learning how to create them. We can do this through how and where we live, our choice of friends, through the vitally important conduct of our family and marital relationships.

In the chapters that follow we shall examine the basic material environment and its life support systems. We shall look at cities and the homes that we try to build in those cities. We shall look in some depth at the personal environment, both intimate and social, and we shall look at what happens when the safe spaces that we need become unsafe. What does radioactivity do to living creatures? What happens in overcrowded cities when the housing is poorly designed and one in two hundred people is carrying the AIDS virus? How do we cope with ill health and unemployment and crime? We shall show how, in a whole variety of ways, we can fail to make the sustaining close contacts with people around us. We shall try to show that change and repair are possible, that we still have a good deal of control over our own spaces and that, particularly in the vitally important social and personal spaces, there is much that we can do to make them not only safe but loving and rewarding.

Quite often this book seems to dwell on what is wrong, but it does not do this in any spirit of despair or pessimism. Quite the reverse – it reaffirms the belief that the human capacity to adapt and change remains undiminished and that, having identified the safe spaces that are essential to life, we shall make them a major priority and seek to ensure that we and others will be able to live with them.

2

CRISIS AND CHALLENGE

For much of the time we are hardly aware of our environment and its importance. Only when things go wrong are we reminded of the delicate balance between us and our surroundings. In order to lead our lives, we require spaces that are safe and free from threat. Nothing reminds us more forcefully of this than the impact of major disasters. The various nuclear pollutants released into the air by the blazing reactor of Chernobyl will, quite apart from the immediate devastation, death and damage, cause an estimated 48,000 new cases of cancer, along with birth defects and other diseases. The gas from the methyl isocyanate tank that escaped into the air of Bhopal, striking the sleeping residents of the city, killed 2,347 people, blinded and seriously injured another 40,000 and led to an Indian Government claim for two billion pounds compensation.[1]

Earthquakes, floods, war and famines unfortunately feature all too often in our daily newspapers and television bulletins. The probing telephoto lens and the on the spot report gives us a comfortable and, at times, detached view of these crises. We see the homeless, the starving, the uniformed doctors and nurses and soldiers. We see the helicopters and the ambulances and the hospitals in tents, and suddenly it's time for the commercial and the quiz show and we might never give the matter another thought. But what about those who are left? What about those who recover? How will they respond to this major disruption of their physical and personal environment? How will they be in a week or a month or next year, with no home or no family?

Buffalo is a small valley in West Virginia, USA. In the early morning of 26 February 1972 a slag dam above the valley gave way, releasing 132 million gallons of water onto the sleeping community below. That murky torrent killed 125 people, injured hundreds and left many thousands homeless. An out-of-court settlement of 13.5 million dollars was paid to the survivors. But there was something very unusual about this payment, for it included 8 million dollars for psychological impairment – acknowledging, for the first time on this kind of scale, that disaster brings with it much more than just physical damage. Two years after the disaster, only one out of every six

5

survivors was free of psychological symptoms. Three-quarters of the survivors still have difficulty in sleeping and two-thirds still have nightmares. Depression, anxiety and personal disruption remained for many.[2]

Natural disasters have been with us for a long time. Early man at the mercy of flood, storm, drought and disease struggled to make sense of his vulnerability and the whimsy of nature. Images of his earliest deities, as seen for example in the grotesque figurines of early Indian civilisation (pre-Harappan) or in the later Kali, offer a menacing and frightening aspect. Nature personified in this way was unpredictable, ruthless, fickle and only intermittently safe and sustaining.[3]

Major crises and catastrophes ultimately make their impact on individuals. The bridge between the material environment and the personal is readily built. Unemployment is us, or somebody we know out of a job. The rising crime rate is our car being stolen or our flat being burgled and vandalised. The earthquake in Mexico was not just a phenomenon of natural history, it was a personal disaster for tens of thousands of people. The poisonous gas that escaped from the chemical plant in Bhopal and the fall-out from the blazing nuclear reactor at Chernobyl struck at ordinary people living in their homes and carrying on with their daily lives. These major disasters affect not only the physical environment but the personal and emotional links that we make with those around us. Our responses to these events can tell us a great deal about ourselves, as well as about our very marked sensitivity to disturbances of the safe space in which we require to live our lives.

When the effects of war, concentration camps and solitary confinement were studied in detail, it was found not only that many people exposed to these brutalities developed symptoms of mental disorder, but that large numbers actually broke down. It became clear that when the conditions are bad enough, threatening enough, or unsafe enough, then people suffer anguish, despair and misery, and often eventually develop either mental or physical illness or both.

Nostalgia was one of the first battle-related conditions to be described.[4] It was first observed among Spanish soldiers fighting in the Thirty Years War in Flanders. These men living under harsh conditions with little chance of leave developed dejection, fever, palpitations and anxiety, all of which disappeared when the soldier was sent home. In later, and perhaps more terrible wars, the documentation of battle-related illness became more detailed. Shell-shock was a chronic syndrome identified in the First World War. One account recalls the fate of men who became mentally ill whilst at the front: 'In World War I neurotics had, as a rule, been kept with the colour until they broke down completely. Some were shot for cowardice, but the example did the others no good ... under strong or continuous stress, no threats of exemplary punishment can prevent breakdowns.'[5]

In the Second World War symptons were present in such large numbers of soldiers during combat that it was difficult to distinguish the mentally abnormal from the normal. It was found that a high proportion of soldiers would break down when about 65% of their companions had been killed or wounded.[6] These breakdowns could range in seriousness from a 'war neurosis' – extreme fear, insomnia and shaking and so on – to marked psychotic disorder with hallucinations and inability to appreciate reality.

Such extremes in the space around us can also cause long-term mental effects. These were first observed in the survivors of the Nazi concentration camps and more recently in soldiers who fought in the Vietnam War. It is now estimated that a quarter of a million veterans have sought treatment for general psychological difficulties which have been labelled as 'post-traumatic stress disorder'.

Just as war affects material space, so death affects interpersonal space, disrupting the close, long-lasting, intimate relationships with others that are a central part of our lives. Most of the studies of disruptive life crises list 'death of husband or wife' (or constant partner) as the most serious and damaging of all. The effects of loss events may be seen in the increased rates of death and illness in the surviving partner of a marriage. Widowers are particularly vulnerable and often really do die of a 'broken heart'.[7]

Our response to bereavement has been divided into three stages. At first there is numbness, in which the bereaved person is stunned and shocked by the loss, and often will not believe it. This gives way to a painful stage of pining in which the lost person is intermittently yearned for. After that, there is the most difficult stage – that of depression. Here despair and emptiness predominate. Life is without meaning and seems pointless without the lost loved one. At this stage bereaved people may try to take their own lives; they are withdrawn and gloomy and Western society marks this by the black of mourning.

Most people gradually overcome these feelings of loss and despair and seek to adjust to the loss and return as best they can to life as it was before the bereavement. For some, however, this stage may drag on so that they never really return to their former style of life – often because they cannot. For others it may worsen till they are overtaken by mental illness, which may be very resistant to medical treatment.

Death is not just about the loss of somebody loved but it is about deprivation. With death, all too often an old order is broken, possibly with nothing to take its place. Here the small nuclear family unity of modern urban society is so much more vulnerable to loss of one member than say the larger extended family groups of older rural societies. The larger family as a functioning system is more resilient and can tolerate much more disturbance.

The bereaved are generally more vulnerable to a variety of physical illnesses and to death itself. In the six months following the death of their wife, men over the age of fifty-five are more likely to die from coronary thrombosis or other vascular diseases than comparable men who have not been bereaved.[9] One study of bereaved relatives in semi-rural Wales found that 4.8% had died within the year compared with 0.68% of a non-bereaved comparison groups.[10] The greatest increase was found among widowers and widows whose relatives had died suddenly and unexpectedly.

The bereaved not only suffer an increased risk of dying after bereavement, they also are more likely to consult their doctor than the non-bereaved. Especially prominent are mental disorders, which are often more intense forms of the 'normal' grief reaction, involving depression of mood, anxiety, muscle tension, pessimism and thoughts of suicide. Bereavement can fundamentally affect not only the safety of our personal spaces but also that of our material spaces. A widow may not only have lost the man she loves but a major contributor to the family income. This grief and sadness are all too often accompanied by fear and panic, aroused by the lack of safety and the anticipated dangers that may follow from that.[11] Supportive family and friends can do much to combat this and restore a feeling of safety, purpose and security.

Imagine the soap operas without death or divorce, adultery or alcoholism. Each week millions of people watch the very rich, and the not so rich, facing problems and crises. We watch them struggling, coping, cracking up, or being written out and we are enthralled. Somewhere in that intrigue is something of you and me, standing up to disturbance of our safe space.

Just as soap operas were really getting a grip on the public imagination, the doctors and scientists began to wake up to what was going on and decided to look more carefully at these threatening and stressful experiences, which they described as 'life events'. It was postulated that certain experiences or events will have a special personal significance for us, which may make adjustment to them particularly difficult. The resulting disruption of our lives may not be associated with emotional distress but may also markedly alter our susceptibility to disease.

A number of investigators set about trying to quantify the effect of these life events. One scale attempted to assess how much readjustment a particular life event would require.[12,13] It gives forty different life events involving change (good or bad) and is scored in terms of the amount of personal adjustment required. Far and away the highest score goes to 'death of a spouse', with divorce, marital separation and death of a family member coming close behind. Losing your job, spending time in jail and retiring from work all score highly. Positive events like marriage, pregnancy, outstanding personal achievement and even taking a holiday also collect quite high scores, all related to the amount of life change they cause. What does this change entail? It is usually a change from something that is established and sustaining and mastered, to something that is unknown and possibly threatening. A change from the safe and secure to the unknown and the unsafe.

Every crisis and every challenge is, of course, different for each one of us.

Bereavement, robbery or bankruptcy may have certain common features, but it is the personal and special significance that the event has for us that, combined with the material consequences, will influence how much it disrupts our equilibrium, upsets our safety and provokes unpleasant emotional feelings.

The route from life events to nervous breakdown is often long and intricate, but for Ranjit P. a few focal events involving his livelihood, personal security and self-esteem caused him to progress rapidly from successful self-sufficiency to psychotic breakdown. He was thirty-two and married with two children. He ran a grocery store in a run-down area of London. It was a small successful business that he had built up over seven years, having saved his wages over many years from previous employment. The shop was just beginning to be successful and a big factor in this was its late night opening and its Sunday trading.

A number of local stall-holders in a nearby market were increasingly jealous of Ranjit's success and although their involvement was never proven, it seemed possible that they had encouraged a group of unemployed youngsters to vandalise his shop. Although no serious damage was done, Ranjit was very shaken and distressed when he found that offensive graffiti had been sprayed onto the glass of his shop, one window had been smashed and faeces had been posted through the letter box. All this presented him with a very considerable challenge, which he tried to meet, but as time passed he began to feel increasingly helpless. He cleaned up the damage, but three weeks after the first attack, as Christmas was approaching, there was a further more serious attack and a paving stone was hurled through the window of his shop causing a lot of damage. He began to feel increasingly tense and suspicious. He found he was unable to trust anyone, even old friends. He went to the police, but although they said they would try to help, they felt there was very little they could do to stop them, as they had no idea who was behind the attacks. After that he started to suspect the police as well.

When threatening letters were posted through his letter box, he decided, in desperation, to sleep in the back of the shop and face his attackers. He was extremely afraid and was neither very large nor skilled when it came to combat. Clearly he was no match for a group of young men bent on causing damage. After three nights in the shop, quite unable to sleep, he started to hear voices threatening him with murder and accusing him of a variety of crimes. He was becoming increasingly exhausted and shaky, his concentration was poor and he was very tense. His doctor prescribed tranquillisers but these did not help and four days before Christmas his premises were attacked again. On discovering this, he picked up an axe and rushed out screaming into the street, threatening passers-by. The police were called and took him to the local hospital, where he was detained against his will for treatment under the Mental Health Act.

His stay in hospital helped, first of all, by giving him sanctuary and safety from the hostile forces outside, giving him space and time to recover his

9

equilibrium and also helping him to develop new strategies and plans to combat the crisis and create a new safety for himself and his family. He underwent fairly intensive treatment for his psychotic disorder with anti-psychotic drugs and counselling. Friends and family rallied round. Gradually his suspicions and his persecutory voices stopped and he started once again to trust people. One of his brothers who lived in Birmingham lent him enough money to start a new business in a different area. He sold the lease of the shop, moved his stores and equipment to new premises, and established a new business and new home for his family in West London. He worked hard and gradually managed to build a new livelihood and a new life for his family and himself, and seemed to make a complete recovery.

Safe space does not come easily to many of us. Frequently life is a battle in which we struggle to find or create conditions compatible not only with survival but with self-expression and satisfaction. As we grow away from the protected spaces in our childhood, we learn to adapt to difficult conditions as well as to face challenges and crises and to cope and to overcome. We are not passive creatures. Once we have defined and identified a problem or threat, we take steps to deal with it.

All too often the life events that really seem to damage us are those that dramatically disturb our safe spaces, thus requiring massive adjustments. Problems are particularly likely to occur if we cannot, because of circumstances, make any significant adaptation or adjustment – as seen in the case of Ranjit. We want to try to adapt, we want to do something, but our life circumstances or the event itself – as say in bereavement – may make it very difficult to take appropriate action.

We come from a long line of survivors; evolution has taken care of that. Our presence here today testifies to the capacity of our ancestors to survive the most unsafe of spaces. When safety is threatened we can, on our own or with others, show an amazing capacity to overcome, to cope, to improvise and master. For some that adaptation in the face of threatening life events, particularly at an early age, may shape the whole of their lives. The demands of the adjustment are so great that long after the damage is past, they go on facing it and adapting to it.

Don McCullin is a photographer, perhaps best known for his pictures of the Vietnamese war. He has travelled extensively in Vietnam and was involved in much of the conflict. In order to get many of his pictures, he had to expose himself to extreme danger and frequently his life has been threatened. His pursuit of danger, uncertainty and excitement, ironically, tells us a great deal about our strange relationship with safety.

Throughout McCullin's childhood his father, whom he loved more than anybody else in the world, was seriously ill. When his father died, the boy was only fourteen and he was devastated. He now had to make his own way amongst the street gangs of North London and was very much on his own while his mother worked to support the family. He says that he grew up on his own in a very unsafe space. He had to stand up for himself and to fight. Gradually he realised that he could face danger and survive, and this became a way of life for him. He was fascinated not only by his own capacity to do this but by that of other people. He became drawn by the extremes of war, the excitement and drama of the battlefield, and by watching what happened to other people in situations where safety seldom existed.

On many occasions he has been very close to serious injury. On one of his last trips he was in PreVeng with the Cambodian Army crawling through an open paddy field. They were ambushed by the Khmer Rouge and he had to lie flat, face down, in a wet paddy field. As he was a photographer, the preservation of his cameras was vital and so, using one hand, he held them up above the water. It was only when the ambush was over that he realised that one of his cameras had been hit by a sniper's bullet. This was obviously intended for him and had come within inches of his face. The experience was utterly terrifying for him and he fell back into the paddy field, completely paralysed with fear, quite unable to move. He escaped, but it took him two years to get his nerve back. People all around him were lying dead in the paddy field and the scene of human devastation was appalling.

Don McCullin deliberately faces danger and tests himself. He says now that it is only extremes, like the ambush in the paddy field, that produce fear. For all that, when he is away he craves to come back to security and safety. The English countryside has a magical quality for him, and it is there, when walking on a still summer day, that he says he really feels safe and secure. He loves to sit by the fire in the evening, with those he loves and is close to. He realises that he has a strange relationship with danger and with safety, and cannot really understand it, although he is quite sure that it all goes back to his early childhood.

This story tells us a lot about ourselves. Going right back to the beginning, it is clear that the personal safety that he enjoyed within his family was destroyed in two ways – by his father's illness and eventual death and by his mother's departure to work. Worse than that, he did not have any kind of secure and supportive circle of friends outside – far from it. He had to face the street gangs of North London. He experienced neither material nor personal safety and grew up in a hostile and uncertain world. He would be the first to admit that, in seeking to adapt, he has over-compensated. Standing up to danger became essential for his survival. Having developed the capacity to do this, he had to go on doing it over and over again, to convince himself endlessly that he could take it.

The study of life events and their significance has revolutionised our thinking about adjustment and illness. Theorists, in a whole variety of disciplines, from medicine to sociology, are becoming more and more convinced that the psychosocial spaces in which we live vitally affect our health. There is an enormous body of research building up which shows that the onset of a whole variety of mental diseases and some physical diseases, such as heart disease, is often associated with life events. Fifty years ago, conditions such as sore throats and the common cold were thought to depend for their existence entirely upon infection from bacteria or viruses. Later it was realised that our susceptibility to infection contributed also, but only recently has it become clear that this susceptibility is greatly influenced by what is going on in our interpersonal and social spaces. Those who have recently lost their jobs, suffered the break-up of their marriage or some kind of crisis are much more liable to suffer from the simple infectious disorders. More serious disorders, such as some kinds of cancer, rheumatoid arthritis, bowel disorder and conditions such as asthma and even appendicitis have been shown, by some investigators, to be related to life events.

It is of course the immune system that is our major defence against infection. This internal bodily system is, in fact, much affected by life events, which, registered by the mind, act through a variety of brain mechanisms to alter bodily function. The study of all this is known as psychoneuroimmunology and it promises to make major contributions to our understanding of a whole variety of diseases.[14] The outset of both schizophrenia[15] and depression has been linked to life events, and attempted suicide has been related to events that threaten or disrupt the safety that we derive from a loved and valued person.[16] A bold and now famous study, known as 'The New Haven Longitudinal Survey', looked at the mental health of one adult selected at random from each of 938 households in New Haven. Indices of mental health were examined in relation to recent life events. In this study there was a clear relationship between mental symptoms and the experience of life events, and the more serious the mental symptoms, the more likely the subject was to have experienced at least one event in the previous year. Even more striking was the finding that if the symptoms worsened, then the subject was more likely to have experienced an increase of life events. This study also found that events involving some kind of loss such as death or divorce or separation were very likely to lead to depression. These events not only involved the rupture of bonds between people, but were also associated with major changes in established patterns of life, leading to a loss of safety and stability. These close relationships are very important to us in a variety of ways. Later we shall explore them in much greater detail.[17]

It's not just negative events that can disturb us or the backgrounds against which we function. A variety of positive events, such as marriage, holidays and promotion can have damaging effects. Marriage may entail a move from an established and possibly satisfactory life as a single person to one that is generally unknown, and that may make a whole variety of new demands upon you. Perhaps deep down you recall that only two out of three marriages survive, and those that do are not all just about the bliss, tranquillity and sensuality that the glossy magazines, with their white smiling brides, offer us.

In the ritual of the annual holiday, the comfort and safety of home with colour television and chips are surrendered for what? An expensive tower block, in a hot country, an unknown distance from the sea, where you stand a higher chance of sun stroke, serious injury in the race for the pool, almost certain delay at one or other airport and episodes of apparently incurable 'tummy trouble'.

The Peter principle – the idea that people are promoted above their level of competence – illustrates the sting in the tail of yet another apparently positive event, a sting that once again usually involves movement from a secure setting with competence and a degree of safety, to something rather unknown. New colleagues, new demands that you may not be able to match. Of course there is the excitement of challenge and the satisfaction of success, but is it not possible that there are also some nagging doubts about the unknown and immediate lack of safety that goes with the promotion?

Not all those who experience these crises will suffer breakdown or illness. Just as our personal lives and out past experiences will help to define the meaning that a particular life event has for us, so too will they influence our vulnerability to life events. In women, both their early experience of intimacy and their current close relationships affect this vulnerability.[19]

Sylvia H. lived in South London. The spaces in which she lived were unsupportive, insecure and continuously changing and threatening. For Sylvia H. any hope of growing up with both her parents in a safe, happy family ceased at the age of seven. Her father was a violent alcoholic who constantly attacked and criticised her mother. Sylvia's earliest memory was of being bruised and hurt as she tried to defend her mother from one of her father's attacks. When Sylvia's mother could bear it no longer, she left home taking Sylvia with her, to find temporary refuge in a hostel for homeless women. Re-housed by the local council, they were soon moved to a flat on an estate accommodating problem families, where conditions were bad.

Their damp flat, with no garden for Sylvia to play in, was surrounded by hostile and aggressive neighbours. Sylvia frequently witnessed violence, sometimes finding her own home broken into and burgled. Sylvia's young world was thus not only materially unsafe but also emotionally very insecure. She was not helped by seeing her mother turn increasingly to alcohol. Short of money Mrs H. paid for her drink by picking up men and bringing them home to the flat. Sylvia clearly remembers at the age of ten being locked in the sitting room and told to watch television. She was well aware of what was going on in the bedroom.

Sylvia began to plot an escape from her mother and the flat she hated. Lacking any skill or qualification, she followed her mother's example and turned to men for material support. At fifteen, longing for freedom, she ran off with Terry, with whom she had a baby. Their relationship went wrong and soon Sylvia left with the baby to move in with another man, Steve, who fathered her second child. With few friends and no supportive family, life was hard and when Steve walked out, leaving Sylvia to cope on her own with two babies, she became desperate and distraught.

The re-appearance of Terry one day threatening to beat her up if she did not hand over his child to him further increased her insecurity. She sank into deep despair and misery. Although she was by no means an ideal mother, she did care very much for her children, who, in turn, gave her the only semblance of continuity and security she had ever known. Desperate to do her best for them, she turned to her local baby clinic for help.

A social worker was alerted to her difficulties and went to see her often at home. Sylvia was rightly very concerned for the welfare of the children but, in addition to her other problems, she was worried that her children would be taken away from her and put into care. She became severely depressed, unable to sleep and in utter despair over the future which was looking increasingly hopeless to her. One evening, after putting the children to bed, Sylvia tried to gas herself in the kitchen oven. However, neighbours raised the alarm in time – Sylvia was taken to hospital and the children put into care with the local authority.

After admission to hospital, even though she was surrounded by people who were supportive and kind, she perceived the world in such a way that she was unable to appreciate or respond to this. It was as if something had shut down within her brain, as if she could no longer see anything good or positive in the world. Sometimes this pervasive pessimism can be due to altered attitudes, but sometimes there is something much more profound that has gone wrong. In Sylvia's case her doctors were fairly confident that she was suffering from a severe depressive illness. This disorder is related to fundamental chemical alterations in the function of mood-relating centres in the brain.

As we shall see from many examples, what begins as something unsafe in the space outside is quite readily translated into physical changes in the physical function of the body. This causal chain from space outside to mind and brain then to body is one that clearly demonstrates our intimate relationships with the material, personal and social spaces in which we live. In depressive illness the altered brain chemistry will sometimes remit spontaneously, but often can only be reversed by the use of mood-altering drugs, known as anti-depressants.

A useful analogy may be drawn between a torn muscle and a strained muscle. Up to a certain point, the muscle may be strained and if given rest and the right kind of bandaging and gentle exercise, it will recover on its own. If, however, a muscle is torn, as say in a skiing accident, then the system is so distorted and changed that it has lost the power to repair itself. Surgical intervention would be required. The skin must be opened, the separated ends of the muscle brought together and sutured, and then there must be complete rest for some weeks, before gentle exercise is begun. We may think of the anti-depressants acting on the brain rather like the surgeon acting on the muscles, affecting the mood-regulating centres in the brain, altering levels of two chemical transmitter substances – 5 hydroxy tryptamine and noradrenalin. This in turn affects various aspects of bodily function, including appetite, sex drive, sleep rhythm and so on.

Sylvia was also encouraged to try to look at the world in a new and more positive way, to make plans, to cultivate some optimism, to see herself capable of positive action. She was seen by a social worker who tried to make some basic changes in her outside environment. First she was given help in the form of basic material security, including a place to live, some financial support and assistance with the children. Secondly she was encouraged to develop social relationships with other people, something she had quite forgotten, and, if all went well, after that to develop more intimate and fond attachments to people.

In due course Sylvia was well enough to leave hospital. She went to live in a hostel for women with similar problems. There she slowly began to make friends and, with a lot of encouragement and support from her new friends, she joined a typing class. This new-found skill gave her confidence, and having increasing access to her children helped as well. She enjoyed being with them again, learning to trust other people and also developing an understanding of her own needs.

In time she was allocated a flat where she and the children lived. With a network of new-found friends and strength drawn from the love and closeness of her children, Sylvia was able gradually to build up a new life for herself. Of course she was depressed at times, but becoming involved with her children's nursery school and helping out in the office typing letters gave her satisfaction and a sense of purpose.

Sylvia's breakdown was due not only to her immediate crisis, but to a lifetime of insecurity and threat. She had been unable to trust her father and received little or no love from him. Her mother let her down too, by running away when Sylvia was seven, so destroying the girl's chances of a loving relationship with her father. When her mother turned to other men, Sylvia had, in effect, lost both her parents. She lacked a sense of security and safety that most of us derive from close relationships with our parents, and she grew up unable to trust other people.

When Sylvia developed relationships of her own, they only fulfilled her worst expectations, being violent, unpredictable and threatening. Trapped by her two young children, she found that her resources became exhausted and she was unable to see any way to help herself. It is not surprising she suffered a breakdown.

It might at first seem strange that earthquakes and infidelity, flood and fires, promotion and poisoning all share something in common. The routine of our daily lives and our survival involves not only the things we own, the buildings we live in and the world outside, but the people we love, the colleagues we work with and the wider social world around us. These form our safe spaces.

In this chapter we have examined both the major dramatic disruption of safe space and the smaller and more personal ones and these we have labelled as life events. We have seen that in some cases life events can be closely linked to the onset of disease. We should be careful, however, not to conclude from this that all disease is either triggered or caused by life events. Even so, the fact that physical disease involving bodily processes can, in certain instances, be set off by disruptions of safe space must alert us to a most extraordinary connection – a connection which we have already described as running from the space outside us to mind and brain and on to the body. This connection will crop up over and over again in such diverse conditions as infections, the so-called auto-immune diseases such as rheumatoid arthritis, in stress diseases such as high blood pressure and two patterns of bodily adjustments to stress – the fight and flight reaction and the general adaptation response.

We show an amazing capacity to adapt to disruption of safe space and the review of disasters in this chapter is not intended to be overly pessimistic, but to remind us that our extraordinary resilience and canniness go hand in hand with a marked sensitivity and vulnerability, something that we often would rather forget and which we try to deny in a whole variety of ways. This uneasy relationship between strength and vulnerability is one that features in the lives of most of us.

3

US IN OUR WORLD

In many small Indian villages you can see what seem to be flat oval cakes about fifteen centimetres across, stuck to the clay walls of the cottages. You will soon discover that these cakes are, in fact, cow dung and they are being dried so that they can be used as fuel for cooking and to provide heat. They therefore help to maintain safe space externally by providing a steady temperature, and contribute to nutrition by helping in the preparation of food. How very ingenious and clever, you might at first think, but if you consider it more carefully you will realise that it is not quite as clever as it seems. It is really rather tragic, in part because its very existence follows from serious mistakes in the past, and its continued practice is going to create a whole new set of problems for the future.

Nobody would choose to burn cow dung. It has to be used for fuel because the trees that once provided wood for fuel have all been cut down, and as no new ones were planted the fuel supply has run out. The dung is rich in nitrogen. When the cows eat grass they are, in effect, removing nitrogen from the soil. In the natural state the dung falls back onto the soil, where it can be used again by fresh growing grass, which will later be eaten by the cows and so on. This is the boring old nitrogen cycle of the fifth form biology class – yet that cycle holds the key to survival for millions of people.

Each cake of dung that is burnt is a cake of dung removed from the soil, and when it is burnt its nitrogen goes up into the air as nitrogen dioxide, being lost (in the short term) to the soil. Plants will not grow in soil with no nitrogen, so before long the cows will have no grass to eat and the villagers won't even be able to burn dung. The short-term demand for energy has been satisfied but the price is the interruption of the nitrogen cycle, with subsequent damage to the soil and eventually the disappearance of plant and animal life from the area. In the short term, the space is safe; in the long term it is becoming very unsafe.

That Indian village is not so very different from the big Western city, whose energy demands require something more than the burning of dried dung. Yet, even though the scale of the enterprises differs, there are two vitally important themes that recur again and again in different disguises. Firstly, our sensitivity to the external physical environment and secondly the costs and benefits that acrue from our attempts to control that environment.

If the household does not burn the dung they will be unable to cook, and if they can't cook they can't eat and will starve. They have the technology in the form of cooking pots and a hearth and when they use that resource effectively the benefit is clear – the whole family gets something to eat. The costs are not so clear, for the last thing that you think about when you are very hungry after a day's work in the fields with day-time temperatures up to 100 degrees Fahrenheit is the nitrogen cycle and the effect of nitrogen depletion on the crop in five years time. When you turn on the television, do you think about how the operators of the atomic power station that generated the electricity are going to dispose of the old fuel rods in a year's time?

One of the reasons why we get so concerned about the safety of the outside spaces is that in a whole variety of ways they affect the space within our body and the cells and organs within it. The intricate structure of our bodies makes it extremely sensitive to external environmental conditions, and in particular those conditions that give basic support to life – air, food, water, external temperature and so on. These environmental supplies support life and help us to maintain constant internal conditions within our body.

The great physiologist Claude Bernard was the first to use the term 'homeostasis'. This literally means same or constant state. He used this term to describe the stable state of the internal environment (*milieu intérieur*) that bodily systems (all the cells of the body) require if they are to carry on functioning. We may think of the interior of the body as a space, within which are the brain, heart, intestine and so on. These organs require a constant temperature, and supplies of oxygen, sugar and so forth, to carry out their particular biological tasks. We have some conscious awareness of the conditions within our body – through simple sensations of hunger, thirst, heat and cold – and these allow us to make certain adjustments. However, some serious disturbances of our internal environment may go undetected.

A good example of this occurs in high blood pressure – a common disturbance of the internal environment. Similarly, the early stages of lung damage secondary to infection such as TB, smoking or air pollution may go quite undetected, only later becoming apparent as breathing difficulties, and shortness of breath on exercise. Any gross disruption of the external environment such as freezing cold or great heat or lack of food or water will, if allowed to disrupt the delicate internal environment of the body, have serious consequences. A primary behavioural imperative for us centres around maintaining external conditions at optimum levels, so that the sensitive internal environment remains constant, allowing vital and life-sustaining bodily systems to operate.

Many adaptations to environmental hazards involve an interplay of conscious action and basic biological regulation systems.[1] Consider the case of

Percy and Theobald – both mad keen on croquet, and playing on a very hot day in the local village fête. After a certain length of time the sensors within Percy's brain begin to register the feeling of heat and, as part of the body's own adjustments, the brain takes steps to deal with the heat problem. In this instance we may think of the brain as a regulator which has been confronted by a deviation from the normal and seeks to return the system to normal limits just as a central heating thermostat would. Heat production is reduced and sweating starts, but lucky Percy also happens to be carrying a multicoloured parasol, he unfolds it and raises it above his head. Within ten minutes he is feeling bright, alert and refreshed and his body is functioning normally once again.

Unfortunately not all men in this situation are carrying multi-coloured parasols and Theobald, who has come out less well-equipped, is unable to get out of the sun and, in spite of all the adjustments that the brain makes to bodily function – sweating, reducing bodily activity, shunting blood to the body surface to encourage heat loss – his body temperature rises and rises. Here a satisfactory adjustment to altered environment has not been possible and a point has been reached where the internal environment becomes hostile and unsupportive to such organs as the heart, brain and so on. The unfortunate Theobald without a parasol develops early stages of heat stroke and eventually collapses and would expire, but a lady also playing croquet is passing and at once gives him her parasol and an iced *citron pressé* that she happens to keep in her first aid box for emergencies such as this, and within a short time his temperature has returned to normal and he is able to return to the game.

Perhaps the most vivid expresssion of lack of safety in the medieval world was seen in the great epidemics of infectious disease. In particular the plague and leprosy deserve a mention because in both cases these disorders struck right at the heart of society, completely ravaging and disrupting its daily existence. A unifying feature of these diseases was their origin in the outside world, in the space that surrounds us which, instead of supporting and sustaining us, harboured bacteria which had the potential to kill us. The Black Death of the fourteenth century is estimated to have killed half the population of Europe.[23] The plague was caused, of course, by a small bacterium. Its principal home was in the rat, but if an infected rat was bitten by a flea, the flea would then carry the disease within it. That flea on biting a human being would transfer the bacteria to them, causing infection which was usually followed rapidly by death. To make matters worse, infected people could transmit the disease directly to others.

Although some basic attempts were made to improve public health, including isolation for up to forty days, at no time were any of the physicians clear about the primary cause of the disease nor, of course, was there any rational treatment. In fact one eminent surgeon, Guy de Chauliac[4] living and practising in Ouvran throughout that time, offered the following treatment recommendations: 'purging with aloes, letting blood, purifying the air with fire, comforting the heart with senna and things of good odour, soothing the humours with Armenian bowl and resisting putrefaction with acid things, carbuncles to be cupped and sacrificed'.

Leprosy, of course, was recorded in biblical times and it caused great difficulties, but because of the slow transmission of the disorder it was easier to contain and isolation was more effective.

There is a great deal of evidence that our own internal state influences our susceptibility to infection. This is usually not a sufficient cause for us to contract an infectious disease. We need not only to be 'run down' but also to come into contact with somebody who is carrying the infectious virus or bacteria. You will therefore not catch mumps unless you breathe in droplets that have been breathed out by somebody carrying the mumps virus. If your body is in a susceptible state and you come into contact with somebody carrying a virus, you may develop the disease. Your immune system provides a natural defence to many infections and also promotes elimination of the virus and prevents further attacks. Some viruses, such as the herpes virus, can be rendered inactive but are not eliminated and the infection may recur from time to time. The virus that causes Aids actually interferes with the function of the cells that are integral to the immune system, preventing natural defences from operating, and leading to a variety of so called 'opportunistic' infections that affect many organs in the body[5] and eventually cause death.

A hundred years ago, many of the most feared diseases were not diseases like cancer or heart disease, but infectious diseases such as tuberculosis, pneumonia or syphilis. People living or working in insanitary conditions lived in dread of infection by bacteria. If a post-mortem attendant or a pathologist cutting up a body accidentally pricked his finger, there was a good chance that he could be dead within days from septicemia. There was not much chance of cure – antibiotics did not exist and once the bacteria had gained access directly to the blood stream, death would rapidly follow.

For many people a century ago, tuberculosis was far more frightening than cancer. A graphic account of the long-term consequences of incurable tuberculosis may be read in Thomas Mann's novel *The Magic Mountain* in which he describes life in a sanatorium high up in the mountains.

Although infectious disease is common today in many parts of the world, energetic public health campaigns in the West and Pacific Basin have eliminated many of the major infectious diseases. Now, with the emergence of Aids, we may be stepping back hundreds of years to the time when infection was a major threat to life. A million Africans are expected to die of the disease over the next ten years[6] and it is estimated that in Uganda one in ten of the adult population is carrying the virus. In the United States 15,000 people have already died of Aids with 180,000 deaths predicted by 1991. At the end of 1986 an estimated 1.5 million people were infected and in New York one in two hundred and fifty is a carrier. In the United Kingdom an estimated 40,000 people are infected[7] and there are around 300 reported deaths at the time of writing.

Just as adaptation involves an interplay of conscious activity and basic biology, so does vulnerability and susceptibility to certain disease. There are six hundred thousand or so deaths each year in the United Kingdom. About half of them are due to disease affecting the heart or blood vessels. Nearly 20 per cent of all deaths are, in fact, due to ischaemic heart disease. Much research supports the idea of a multi-factorial basis for these conditions. Some, like genetic predisposition, which is undoubtedly a major risk factor, cannot be modified by the individual. It does seem, however, that there are a number of risk factors which lie, at least in part, within our voluntary control. These include nutritional factors, exercise, cigarette smoking and a broad range of personal and relationship factors. There is much evidence to support the existence of a vulnerable personality type – type A. These individuals are very time-concious and continually set themselves goals that are demanding or difficult to attain. Achievement often fails to satisfy them. They are competitive and striving. Other studies suggestion that insensitivity to their own emotional state and competitive unsupportive marital relationships also contribute.

The earliest sign of cardiovascular disorder is usually some mild elevation of the blood pressure and a conspicuous absence of symptoms. Examination may reveal some degree of stress, tension, hyperventilation, obesity or hyperchondriasis. Occasionally there may be diminished exercise tolerance and sometimes the suggestion of early cardiac pain.

There is some evidence that at this early stage a number of interventions may be effective. These will particularly involve altering those risk factors that are within the control of the individual. Major modifications of work, marital relationships and personal ambition may be necessary. Just as modifying your sexual behaviour will affect your risk of contracting Aids, so changing your smoking behaviour affects your risk of contracting lung cancer. By altering the internal environment of your lungs, you profoundly affect the function of the cells within them. The smoke that you inhale will first affect the delicate cells that line your respiratory passages. The fine hair-like structures on these that clean the lung are paralysed by the smoke so that old mucus and irritants accumulate in your lungs. This offers a variety of bacteria an ideal site in which to grow. They start to multiply in your lungs and soon you will have a bad cough and bring up green sputum. You have bronchitis, which may later develop into chronic bronchitis. If you continue to smoke you have a high chance of contracting lung cancer. In their 1968 Report, the Royal College of Physicians estimated that 90 per cent of deaths from lung cancer and 75 per cent of deaths from chronic bronchitis were attributable to cigarette smoking.

Although infection may be returning to the West, starvation is not, but in spite of this, 1985 saw an extraordinary shift in public awareness of this most devasting of environmental hazards. One of the most significant social phenomena of the decade was the emergence of the Live Aid Movement. All at once, affluent countries of the globe not only became aware of the starving families of Africa, but also allowed themselves to feel for them and, even more important, to do something for them. The generation that began to care about its own body, health, fitness and the food it ate, was suddenly ready to realise that it was responsible for other people on the planet and able to do something for them. Survival was no longer taken for granted. Salvation was not just about good conduct, or kicks, it was also about helping others to find a place in this overcrowded world, and doing something to better that world. Perhaps humanity's view of itself is just beginning to change. We are beginning to see ourselves not just as minds, or souls, but as whole people living in a material world where food and fuel and pollution and survival are real issues. This new awareness of ourselves and our world has important implications for the way we try to understand our health, behaviour and what we are.

On that important evening when Bob Geldof was watching his television he saw, as many of us did, those unforgettable pictures of starving babies in Ethiopia. Too weak to move, they were dying in their mothers' arms, with flies buzzing on their scarcely living bodies. We all saw the same thing yet he saw behind the suffering to its cause. He saw that without the right environment, without the right conditions, without food, these people would surely die and, when he saw and realised this, he set out to do something about it. Soon he was not alone.

The Live Aid Movement was, of course, specifically directed at the plight of the Third World and those starving in Ethiopia. It vividly emphasised that, whilst in the West many people eat too much, most of the world is still short of food and many are starving. Oxfam estimate that malnutrition currently affects 750 million people, whilst water-related diseases affect a similar number. The basic material spaces in which these people live remain fundamentally unsafe and are not supportive to life.

In many parts of the world, technology in combination with wealth has eliminated many basic environmental hazards and supplies a balanced diet, clean water and a place to live. However, even in the 'richer' countries of the world the wealthy still enjoy much better health than those who are less well off.[8] There is no single more important contributor to our safety and survival than energy. The harnessing and discovery of various forms of energy has completely altered our position within the planet and our ability to manipulate our environment.

For the last two hundred years the major source of energy for indusrial and domestic purposes has, of course, been fossil fuel, initially coal and then more recently oil.[1] These are non-renewable resources that, at the present rate of consumption, will be nearing exhaustion by the twenty-first century. The combustion of these fossil fuels produces large quantities of carbon dioxide.

Previously the carbon dioxide that was cycled derived mainly from that which was exhaled by living creatures such as us and our various animal relatives. Now, with the advent of the motor car and coal-burning power stations, vast quantities of carbon dioxide are entering into the cycle. These cannot possibly be recycled by plant photosynthesis, and of course the destruction of the rain forests aggravates the problem. It has therefore been suggested that atmospheric levels are going to carry on rising, eventually leading to a 20 to 25 per cent increase above the current average by the year 2000. The presence of this high concentration of carbon dioxide in the atmosphere will lead to an increased absorption of solar energy, reflected from the earth's surface, particularly in the longer wavelengths. This re-absorption of solar energy will in turn lead to an increased atmospheric temperature – the so-called 'greenhouse' effect' – which will bring about the melting of the polar ice caps, disastrously diminishing the amount of land available for habitation.

At the same time as the greenhouse effect, the other components of fossil fuel combustion, such as smoke and other particles, will have the opposite effect so that there will be a reduction in solar energy and a fall in temperature. Either way, it looks as if the continued combustion of fossil fuel could well have very serious consequences.

As you are reading this book you are continuously breathing. With each breath, you take in not only the basic gases of the atmosphere – nitrogen, oxygen, carbon dioxide and a number of inert gases – but also a whole variety of other substances that you cannot see or sense. If you live in the inner cities it is very likely that you will be taking in a whole variety of by-products emitted from the combustion of petrol and the burning of coal. Occasionally, some of these become visible during the infamous smogs of Europe and the United States. Los Angeles, of course, is particularly famous for these smogs[1].

A dramatic and extremely unpleasant manifestation of atmospheric pollution is now to be seen in the form of acid rain. This is caused by the presence of sulphur dioxide and oxides of nitrogen in the atmosphere. This collects in various areas and then falls to the ground or is washed down to the ground in rain or snow. It destroys living creatures in lakes and streams as well as vegetation. Vast areas of forest, developed over thousands of years, are now within short spaces of time being wiped out and whole areas are turning into desert. At the present rate of destruction, there will be no trees at all left in Austria by 1997.[9] The acid appears to be accumulating in the soil so that even immediate control, which is in any case unlikely, would not now halt the damage for some years.

It is not just the motor car and the coal-burning power stations that are involved. A variety of chemical plants and processes, along with such things as refuse burning, combined to release into the atmosphere literally millions and millions of tons of hydro-carbons, natural gases, solvent vapours and other materials each year.[1] An idea of the scale of the problem may be gathered from considering the output of one thousand cars operating for a single day. These will produce over three tons of carbon monoxide, six hundred pounds of organic vapours and about one hundred and fifty pounds of nitrous oxide.[10] Another important pollutant from motor cars is, of course, lead. This has recently been attracting a good deal of attention as it is now becoming fairly clear that even low concentrations affect the brains of young children and may well impair intelligence. As part of exhaust emission from engines, it enters the atmosphere, where it is inhaled, while some falls to the ground in rain, which is then drunk and incorporated into the food chain. The lead gets into the blood, accumulates in bones and teeth, and has particularly serious effects on the developing central nervous system.

Those of us living in the developed and industrialised countries of the world take it for granted that when we turn on the tap, water will flow forth. This water is said to be drinkable and is generally free from the more serious bacterial contaminants which, in the cities of the Middle Ages and even later, caused outbreaks of food poisoning, dysentery and so on. In the industrialised countries of the world, we consume, on average, between two hundred and two hundred and fifty litres of water per person per day, and this consumption requires a massive amount of recycling. This recycling has to deal with a whole variety of pollutants which include sewage and a whole variety of chemicals which enter the water supply from polluted rivers. The water that we ultimately drink may be free of the more dramatic disease-causing bacteria, but is certainly not free of small quantities of detergent, bleach, hormone, dye, insecticides and small traces of other material whose ultimate effect on our health remains generally unclear.[1]

The food we eat may also be contaminated or polluted and dramatically affect our health. Infected food, often meat or cream, may cause diarrhoea and vomiting which, in the young in hot countries, cause fluid depletion and can be life-threatening. The pursuit of 'safe food' has been an energetic one. There are a vast number of techniques for preserving and stabilising food, and these involve not only various physical processes like freezing and radiation, but also the use of a whole range of chemicals which include such potentially dangerous substances as sulphur dioxide, sodium nitrate and benzoic acid. Other food additives include emulsifiers, stabilisers, anti-oxidants and solvents. These substances are concerned mainly with the preservation of the food. Apart from these, there are substances which make the food appear, at least outwardly, more desirable to us. These substances are used to provide colour, flavour or sweetness.[1] The consumer magazine *Which?* identified one 'cake' – a 'Black Forest gateau' – which contained twenty-three different additives.

The adverse consequences of these substances range from stomach cancer to asthma and allergy in children. In many cases their long-term effects have yet to be elucidated, but it is becoming increasingly clear that the enlightened consumer has had enough and is fleeing, in desperation, to so-called 'health foods'. Unfortunately these foods too are not always as healthy as they seem and may contain all kinds of pollutants that have entered the food chain through the soil.

Tezcatlipoca ('Smoking Mirror') was the Aztec god of the Sun, who ripened the harvest but who also could bring drought and sterility. This most feared and awful god each year received as a sacrifice the still beating heart of a man – cut from him in a single stroke by the officiating priest.[11] Four thousand years ago the ancient British druids built Stonehenge to celebrate the summer solstice and to make sacrifice to the Sun God.

Human sacrifice is found in a whole variety of cults and culture. It was carried out in honour of the Molochs of Carthage, certain Braziliarn deities, and was also reported by Caesar as being practised amongst the ancient British. Human sacrifice is often closely linked with cannibalism, in which the strength and power of the poor victims, rather than being used to appease, placate or feed the petulant gods, is instead required to energise or rejuvenate those who consume their own kind. As recently as 1950, the Fore tribe in New Guinea ate their dead relatives in pursuit of their strength and wisdom. What they did not realise was that within them there was a slow and resilient virus that, over some twenty years, caused a fatal disease known as kuru, a disorder closely resembling Parkinson's disease and accompanied by dementia and eventual death.[12]

In the twentieth century human sacrifice has been outlawed, but many societies now stake their long-term survival on a mysterious source of power, whose qualities, in some ways, are so awesome that it is not entirely unlike the various sun gods worshipped and sacrificed to by Aztecs, Romans, druids and so on, whose power energised the world and brought food from the soil. This substance is not a god or a sun, and it does not demand human sacrifice, although many believe and predict that human sacrifice will be an inevitable consequence of its widespread use. This substance of course is uranium, a source of energy so potent that one kilogram can provide the same energy as the burning of 3,000 tonnes of coal.

This energy is derived from the forces that hold together the sub-atomic particles that comprise uranium. Under controlled conditions uranium 235 is bombarded with neutrons, causing the breakdown of the substance and the release of vast quantities of heat energy. The radioactivity, the high heat production and the tendency of the reaction to become self-sustaining and the problems with the waste products make this form of energy production a risky business, although its proponents maintain all these risks can be anticipated and controlled. As the demand for energy gets ever greater and the stores of fossil fuel begin to run down, atomic power seems, for many, to be god-like and to offer an almost infinite source of energy.

The energy emitted from radioactive substances is able to penetrate most materials and inflicts a particularly serious kind of damage upon the living cell. It exerts its major effect on the DNA – the strands of protein that contain the genetic code of the cell and enable it to reproduce itself. This makes fast-dividing tissues in the body, such as white blood cells, especially vulnerable and also places cells involved in reproduction at particular risk. The two major effects of radiation are cancer and genetic defects.

Survivors of the atomic bombs that ended the Second World War in Japan showed an increase in the incidence of leukaemia.[13] New cases were still emerging twenty-five years after the bombs had dropped. Cancers of the breast, bone, lung and thyroid are also associated with radiation. Workers in uranium mines are particularly susceptible to such lung cancers,[14] whilst children exposed to radiation may develop thyroid cancer[15] up to thirty years after exposure.

The genetic effects are much more difficult to quantify, particularly at low levels of exposure, but animal experiments using high doses clearly demonstrate damage to chromosomes and dramatic rises in birth defects following exposure to radiation. Investigations of the population living around nuclear reactors[16] suggest that rates of certain cancers may be higher than those found in the general population. As well as the long-term damage, the risk of accident is ever present. On the nights of the 25 and 26 April 1986, what apparently began as a series of illegal and unauthorised experiments on the no. 4 reactor at Chernobyl led to fire and loss of control of the nuclear reactor and was soon to become the worst nuclear accident in history, causing thirty-one short-term deaths and possibly 6,000 cases of cancer in the USSR alone. Other estimates have given much higher figures, with possibly 200,000 eventual deaths from cancer in the USSR.[17] The generating station was only twelve miles from a town of 40,000 inhabitants, and Kiev, one of the largest cities in the USSR, was ninety miles away. At one stage, there was a very real possibility of a melt-down that would have contaminated almost the entire water supply of the city of Kiev and then spread down to the Black Sea.[18]

Large quantities of radioactive waste were emitted into the atmosphere, affecting not only Russians but also people living in Poland, Sweden, Italy and Great Britain. Nuclear power would never be the same, for that single disaster focused the eyes of the world onto the enormous risks and costs involved in extracting energy from nuclear reactions. There have been many nuclear accidents. On 8 October 1957 there was a serious fire at the Windscale plutonium production reactor. Human error was entirely responsible and once the fire had started, nobody was sure how to put it out or even that it could be put out. Three days later it was out, but not before it had released large quantities of radioactive isotopes into the atmosphere.[19]

Radioactive substances pose particularly severe threats because they become readily incorporated into various naturally occurring systems and cycles. Radioactive iodine, once it is present in sea water, rain or soil, behaves exactly like ordinary iodine and will be present in the food we eat and the water we drink. It then becomes incorporated into our metabolic pathways and concentrated in our thyroid glands. Young children are particularly vulnerable.

Some radioactive substances go on being radioactive and therefore dangerous for hundreds or thousands of years and for up to five hundred thousand years in the case of plutonium. Plutonium is the most dangerous by-product from atomic technology, especially as it is also the one that remains radioactive for the longest time, with a half-life of nearly twenty-five thousand years. This means that if one gram of plutonium is deposited in the soil, half a gram will still be intensely radioactive after twenty-five thousand years, a quarter of a gram after another twenty-five thousand years, and so on. Some fairly sophisticated mathematics will indicate that one millionth of a gram will still be left after five hundred thousand years.[20] This quantity, although small, is still extremely dangerous, causing considerable genetic and cellular damage to any living organism that comes into contact with it.[20] No science fiction is needed here. This invisible hazard is everywhere in increasing concentrations. Each day more and more radioactive material is actually being produced, in spite of the fact that there is no safe and effective way of disposing of that material.

In the UK alone there are now one thousand cubic metres of high activity radioactive liquid, stored in steel tanks and requiring constant agitation and cooling because of the very considerable heat production.[21] By the year 2000 there will be three times this amount to be stored. In whose back garden will it be placed, under whose village or town or common will the next completely safe dump be made? Would most of us say, 'It doesn't matter as long as it's not near me!' and 'I'm happy to go on using the comforts made possible by the power generated'? The demonstrations against the burial of nuclear waste seem to have been small local affairs attracting little public support or interest.[22]

Apart from the inevitability of nuclear contamination, there is every chance that there will be other nuclear accidents. The Chernobyl disaster nearly happened in the USA at the now famous Three Mile Island site. In spite of this, in the UK plans are now under way to build a second water-cooled reactor at Sizewell next to the existing gas-cooled type. Sizewell is eighty-four miles from London and it has been suggested that an accident there could result in fatal cancer in 24,000 Londoners and 3.5 million people being evacuated from the capital. How many more Chernobyls can the world take? We can't clean the world like a dirty room, or exchange it for a new one like an old car. This is it – this is the only world we have.[23]

As we have seen with the smogs and the greenhouse effect, fossil fuels are not free of risk, but with nuclear installation the risks are especially great and many would say quite unacceptable. As this brief review shows, many of our attempts to achieve safety in one area result in the disappearance of safety in another. The benefits are often obvious, dramatic and alluring, but the costs are just beginning to be realised and all too often they are equally dramatic and anything but alluring.

There is nothing new about human demands on the planet. Ten to fifteen million years ago Ramapithecus, one of our distant ancestors, may have moved from the dense tropical forest where he swung by his arms to more open woodland. His descendants continued the progression out into open grassland where, two to three million years ago, Australopithecus may have used very simple tools and weapons to hunt small rodents and even small apes.[24] Now still in need of the same basic life support systems, we have to compete for resources with 4,500,000,000 other human creatures. Now we operate in a vast net of cultural elaboration and employ technology in every area of our relationship with the planet to satisfy our ever growing demands.

Book 1 of The I Ching, the Ancient Chinese Book of Changes, makes reference to the image of a lake which can only hold a limited amount of water – too much and the lake will overflow:

> Limitations are troublesome, but they are effective. If we live economically in normal times, we are prepared for times of want. To be sparing saves us from humiliation. Limitations are also indispensable in the regulation of world conditions.[25]

The challenge of the cultural explosion of the last five thousand years has been competition and survival. The challenge of the next fifty will be co-operation, restraint and limitation.

4

SAFE SPACE AND LIVING SYSTEMS

Seen from a satellite or space craft, our world has an eerie organic quality about it, with its blues and greens and moving white clouds – it almost looks like a living thing. Life thrives and flourishes in a narrow layer of organic matter on the surface of the dead and rocky substance that comprises the crust of the earth. That branch of science concerned with the conditions that particular living things require for survival is ecology. It is derived from the Greek word oikos – a home or a house.

Looked at overall, the human population and the world may be seen as part of a giant and finely balanced ecological system. We are that mass of humanity and our imperative is survival and the conditions that favour survival, which will include food, shelter, constant temperature and so on. There are now 4,864 million of us living on the earth and the population is increasing so rapidly that by the end of the century there could be between 7,000 and 8,000 million people on this planet. Two hundred years ago the population of the world was 1,000 million people.

An ecological view emphasises the close interrelations between all living matter and the processes or systems that are life itself. The food we eat passes through our digestive systems, which is able to extract from it all that we need for survival. The waste product, rich in nitrogen, enters back into the nitrogen cycle to be used yet again by bacteria, insects and growing plants to produce yet more food, sustain life, and ultimately to produce new human beings. In the UK, up to 40 per cent of treated sewage finds its way back to the fields as fertiliser, which is in turn absorbed by the plants which are then eaten by us and so on. When we die, we too, like the digested food we have produced all through our lives, eventually pass into that nitrogen cycle, and into a number of other cycles, so that eventually the very molecules that made us will make plants, animals and other human beings.

Here the Hindu Wheel of Life is made real. It is myth, but its message, as with so many myths, echoes an important reality. Long ago we were constrained by our very limited technology and guided by the morality of holy books. These books were not written for the science of the third millennium.

SAFE SPACE AND LIVING SYSTEMS

We must find new paradigms and new morality to help us set limits and make sense of our world. Ecology may not be mystical but it can serve as myth once did to guide us and to help us find a way to exist harmoniously with our planet. We need the old myths but we also need the insights and ideas of science, not arrogant, self-centred science, but science of the human scale that knows its place in the world.

Over thirty thousand years the emphasis of our venture has been on getting what we require from the world. Only very recently have we realised that the energetic exploitation of the world is beginning to upset the balance of the world's ecology, causing, in the fairly short term, a major threat to our survival.[1]

This ecological awareness demands that our pursuit of a satisfactory relationship with the environment should not be pursued without regard to the effects on the environment.[2] Our immediate demand for safe space might prompt us to cut down most of a five-hundred-year-old forest over a period of a few years. This might give us and our group safe space over that short period, but the speed of cutting and the difficulty of replacing the trees would result in the complete destruction of the forest. For us, our children and everybody else, as well as every other creature, that place would no longer be available as a wood and the space would become very unsafe, unable to support life or provide resources.

This is exactly what is happening not only to the tropical rain forests of Brazil, but also to the forests in many countries of the world. Our own basic domestic activities, such as reading newspapers, building houses and burning wood for fuel, are beginning to have consequences for the functioning of the whole planet and all the creatures living upon it. The very air we breathe is at risk. The carbon dioxide cycle described in the last chapter is being disrupted, so that in time there will be insufficient wood and, even more important, insufficient oxygen.

We can, as one study did,[3] look at major components of the system, such as population, capital expenditure, natural resources, pollution and capital investment in agriculture, and then using a fairly powerful computer, see what happens to the system when the variables start to change. What will happen to our need for natural resources when, by the end of the century, the population has doubled? What will happen to the population when, in about five to ten years time, the oil and petrol supplies begin to run out?

Ecology is one of those rather new sciences which studies processes rather than things. Ecology looks at relations across time, at change and at system. An ecology of persons, or a human ecology, will look at the individual as a moving, changing entity, a living system existing in a variety of spaces. As with all living creatures, our most basic task is to resist entropy, which is the tendency of all matter in the universe to revert to a simpler and lower energy state. All living creatures are in rebellion against this; using energy and information, they

30

assemble and consolidate and resist disintegration.

The whole person is a living system, committed to a whole variety of functions from breathing to locomotion – but that whole is itself made up of a vast collection of smaller units which themselves operate as systems. The understanding of biological systems is pursued into general systems theory. Some of its ideas and principles will be used in a descriptive way here – though in a rather loose sense – and at times we shall deviate from the strict technical sense in which its jargon is used by scientists.

Systems may be interrelated in a variety of ways, but the most basic way to view functional interrelations is in terms of hierarchy. Consider a factory with a managing director at the top, beneath him executives, below him managers, then foremen, then workers. At each level in the factory there is a degree of autonomy – managers can to some extent operate on their own, but at times they will need to refer up or down the tree, or operate in relation to other parts of the tree. They may not increase production without information from the executive and neither can they, in functional terms, achieve that increase without cooperation from the workers beneath them.

As with the company, the functional parts of our bodies are organised in a hierarchy. At the lowest level are giant molecules, which combine to form cells, while collections of cells make organs, and groups of organs make organ systems.[4] Finally, a group of organ systems linked by the control and communication system of the nervous system make a single, separate and whole independent being. At each level there is a degree of independence.

A red blood cell carries oxygen by itself – thus it is an autonomous system. Yet it can only carry oxygen if the respiratory system takes in enough oxygen through the lungs to supply it. At a higher level, the nervous system can only function if the red blood cells keep it well supplied with oxygen. Without this the brain will stop working and we will faint and may suffer brain damage or death if the deprivation is prolonged. The red blood cell operates on its own to transmit oxygen, but is dependent on the respiratory system supplying it, and at the same time is a vital contributor to the larger and more intricate nervous system.

We, as whole beings, are not so dissimilar to the lowly red blood cell, for although we can operate to a limited extent on our own, we are dependent on other groups of people and the world in general for some of our needs, and in conjunction with others we also comprise larger functioning systems such as the family unit, social groups, town city and so on.

The most obvious division of human systems will be into biological and social. Most biological systems operate within the space of the body – for example, the circulatory and nervous systems – while others operate not only within the body, but also within the material space of the outside world. The respiratory system is a good example of this, the lungs offering up to the atmosphere a giant surface area, about the size of a tennis court, across which gases pass. The simplest system of social organisation is, of course, the dyad or two person relationship. This operates in material space, but by stretching the idea of space a little, we can also think of it as operating in an abstract space of emotions, values, beliefs and so on, which we hope are shared by the two people involved in the social system or relationship.

When two people are dancing closely, the space in which they dance cannot be adequately described simply by reference to the size of the room, the temperature of the air and the loudness of the music. Their feelings for each other, their moods and what they know about each other will also be of vital importance in understanding the operation of this social system. We may call this 'interpersonal space' – the space between and around two people. Only by expanding our description in this way can we distinguish between an affectional system operating between two lovers, and an economic system operating between a call girl and her client.

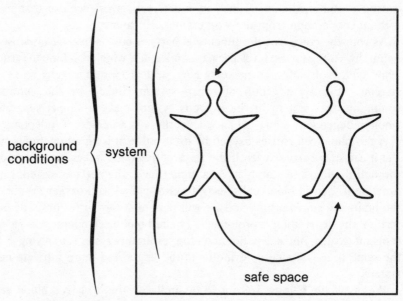

A two-person system operating in background conditions that are 'safe' — that is, conditions that are sustaining and free from obvious threat

The use of the word space in the book's title is closely related to this system's approach. A space is a loosely defined area, within which a system operates. Some systems operate in a space that is closed off from the world outside. A typical closed system is the gearbox of a car, sealed in its steel gearbox and bathed in thick oil. The gears function to alter the transmission of engine power to the wheels. As long as the background conditions of the space in which it operates, such as oil and temperature, are kept within certain limits, the system will function. Most of the systems that we shall consider operate in living creatures or in nature. They occupy spaces that are less well defined and insulated. These systems are then open to a variety of external influences and are known as open systems.

A safe space loosely defined for the purposes of this book is a space of environment whose qualities permit certain systems to operate. A safe space is therefore not only a space where conditions are good enough for the system that occupies it, but a space that is free of any threatening or damaging process that might eventually interfere with the system's operations.

Let us summarise our observations so far. We can usefully view ourselves as living systems. At the same time we are components in other larger systems which may be either biological or social. Any system may be thought of as operating in spaces within certain loosely defined boundaries. Within spaces certain conditions prevail, and conditions that are good enough for the system to function adequately may be called 'safe spaces'.

Where is all this taking us? We can now begin to link the system's approach with the broad survey of the first two chapters. It is safe space that we seek in our world, and it is safe space that crises and life events disrupt. We can begin to see why we need clean air, pure water and uncontaminated food. We shall see what links our sensitivity to drought and radioactivity. We can begin to see that bereavement and divorce or separation or violence can so disrupt our functioning that they can lead on to mental or physical illness, for – just like physical disruption – they can cause major upset to the function of personal or social systems. All these observations and facts relate to a central theme. This theme tells us the conditions that we all need if we are to begin to lead normal and reasonably acceptable lives. Having looked at what happens to us when conditions are not right, we can begin to build up a picture of what the right conditions might be like.

Let us now change our approach and, instead of looking at what our surroundings do to us, let us briefly look at what we do to our surroundings. What do we want from the world outside? Does safe space feature in normal life – do we pursue it or care about it? Does it matter to you and me in our daily lives? What moves and drives us? What do we need and want from other people and from the environment in which we live?

Many of the early answers to these questions were given by the first psychologists who sought to be rigorously scientific and called themselves behaviourists. They formulated simple reward theories, in which human beings were likened to white rats in laboratories, pursuing food for reward and avoiding other things in order to escape punishment. There certainly are control systems in the human brain which work using this very simple paradigm, and each and every one of us is aware of behaviours that conform to this pattern. However, the story is much more complex.

In the 1950s and 1960s, as a revolt against this, some psychologists postulated 'need' theories[5] and suggested a hierarchy of needs which they arranged in order of importance: physical needs – security needs – love needs – esteem needs – self-actualisation needs. The most basic of physiological needs involved such things as hunger, thirst and sleep. Security needs involved financial and physical stability and love needs involved the search for powerful links with other individuals.[6]

There were many modifications of need theory, and a second approach, known as goal theory, gradually emerged. This shifted the emphasis back to the individual. Goals involve aims that people set for themselves. One individual may continuously seek to establish strong and satisfying relationships with others, while another may put power, mastery and dominance as his most important aim in life and consciously pursue these. The goal then is rather like an intention to travel somewhere. A man's goal may be to become Head of the Bank of England – something that he will seek to achieve across time.

These two approaches of course developed alongside the much earlier work of the psychoanalysts, with their emphasis on early childhood, security and attachment and the psycho-biologists, who were superseded by the attachment and the life event theorists, whose work we looked at in the first chapter. Quite apart from these theories, there were hosts of other ideas from sociologists, ecologists, ethologists, philosophers, theologians and others. Many of them seemed to be saying very important things about us and our relationship with our surroundings, yet each school on its own seemed to be telling only a small part of the very complex story, rather like the curious villagers in the famous Suffi story of the elephant.[7] A travelling show brought an elephant to a small village. On the night of its arrival, curious villagers crept in the darkness into its cage to try to discover the nature of this strange beast. In the black of night each man could only feel a different part of the elephant and when they returned to their village to compare results, their widely differing descriptions, relating to trunk, tail, legs and belly, produced confusion and disorder.

In fact we now know that the whole elephant cannot be described and anyway the scope of our project is much more complex than describing the elephant. For all its shortcomings, though, the story urges us in the right direction, encouraging us to utilise a variety of viewpoints and to try to integrate them in pursuit of broader or more holistic views. By looking at ourselves as a collection of systems operating in a variety of spaces from biological to personal, we will perhaps be getting closer. We will be just as interested in the report of the size of the elephant's trunk as in the report of how the elephant goes to sleep and the way it arranges the straw beneath it before doing so.

Although some of this sounds rather obscure, it is really quite easy to look at ourselves in terms of systems and spaces with the aid of a chart or map. The basic structure of the chart may be seen in the diagram with the body and self at the centre, occupying a variety of spaces. These may be most simply divided into material, personal, social and mental.

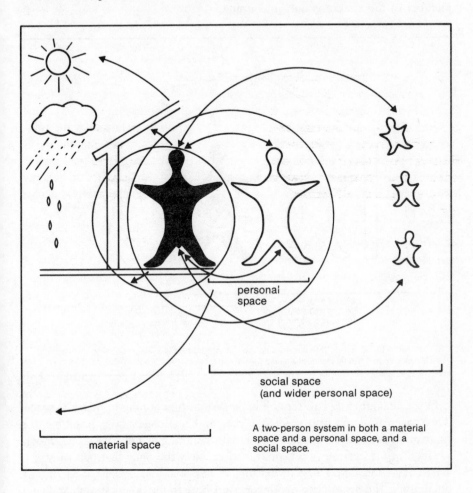

personal
space

social space
(and wider personal space)

A two-person system in both a material
space and a personal space, and a
social space.

material space

You may draw yourself at the centre, living in the material space of your room, in the larger space of the world outside with sun, rain and air. On the other side we can define intimate/personal space and beyond, the wider social space. Once we have drawn the map, we can draw in particular systems which happen to concern us. We might draw in the intimate, affectional system involving you and your co-habitee. We might also draw in two children and a friend who lives in the same house as part of a wider family system. We could draw in the house as part of the living system.

We can then identify any lack of safety in the space which is upsetting the operation of the system. We can also, of course, define defects of the system itself. If you live in a damp house with a leaking roof, this defect of the material space may be identified. If it then makes your co-habitee ill, the family system will start to break down, not just because of the environment but also because a member of the system is not functioning.

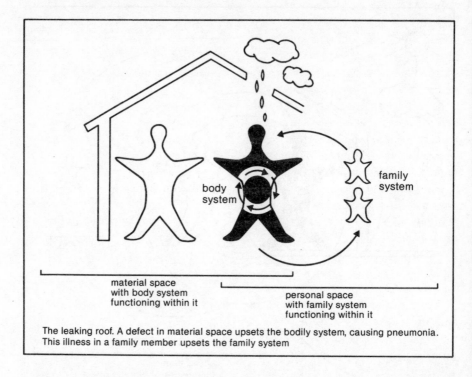

The leaking roof. A defect in material space upsets the bodily system, causing pneumonia. This illness in a family member upsets the family system

In the diagram you can see the body system functioning in material space. This space is damp and cold and wet, and no longer safe, upsetting the function of the body as a system, eventually resulting in a disease – pneumonia – which in turn seriously impairs function. Now the body that becomes ill is also part of the family system existing in personal and social space. Ill with pneumonia, the person can no longer contribute to the family system and goes to bed with lemon juice, brandy, vitamins and so on. The family system starts to break down, with one critical member missing from it. Luckily there is an additional adult in the home who can enter the family system and maintain it.

Because this map shows us how to draw in both systems and the spaces in which they work, it is particularly well suited to expressing the detailed effects of disease or illness.[8] It can not only show disease as an upset within a bodily system, but can also trace its effects into other spaces and systems. A broken leg removes a major part of the locomotion system and prevents movement, but it may affect a whole variety of other systems – perhaps involving family, work and leisure. The true story of the damage involves much more than just describing the physical lesion. All too often an apparently trivial illness has effects that can only be understood by following its effect in this way. We shall explore this approach in greater detail in Chapter 10, which is about safety in illness.

Just as a broken leg can upset the family system, so can a major dispute between two family members. The wrong emotions or feelings can cause the system to stop functioning just as readily as pneumonia or any other serious illness. The family system needs safe personal space as well as safe material space. That personal space is created by emotions, feelings and attitudes, and within it two or more people relate.

The chart can remind us of our strengths and resources – social supports and networks can be drawn in, as can material resources. The chart can also be used to help us to define goals and direction and movement. It is particularly well suited to helping us to understand how a breakdown in one system can radically affect function in other systems.

Janet S. works as a casting director for a small film company. The company goes bankrupt so that her work system loses the space in which it operates. Without this it cannot function – Janet loses her job. Her demoralisation causes her to withdraw from her friends, leading to a breakdown of her friendship and support system, and her lack of income, despair and isolation rapidly affect the function of the family system. In time her health is affected, depression develops and she eventually requires medical treatment for this.

A similar story has already been explored in the story of Sylvia in Chapter 2, and further expansion of these themes will be pursued in the later chapters of the book. At this point the details are not important; what is important is the way the chart allows us to see clearly the interrelation between all these apparently rather different aspects of our lives.

Another special strength of the space and systems approach which can be seen in both these stories is the way that it allows us to move readily into the space of the body and look at the systems within it. Frequently, as with the leaking roof, events in the outer material or personal spaces will lead to changes in the internal workings of the body and eventually to disease itself. The heart and its vascular system are particularly liable to be adversely affected by what begins as a series of upsets in social or personal systems or their spaces. We will explore this in more detail in Chapter 5.

Finally we must make some reference to a space called mind. This space, although abstract, provides, as we shall see, a very important component of our environment. Within this space operate systems of belief, desire and goals that will profoundly affect not only what we do in the world but the way in which we do it. Here we can include our more personal beliefs and intuitions as well as our involvement with wider global belief systems such as religious and political belief. We are not concerned here with specialist tools for precise measurement but rather with the pursuit of general truths about ourselves and our place in the world. In assessing our own position in the world, we can make reference to the fundamental dimensions of safe space and assess, within each one of them, how any particular system functions. Once we have identified problem areas, we will be in a much better position to take some positive action and seek appropriate help.

The chart is particularly useful when a number of things go wrong at the same time. Rather than simply dealing with a global crisis, we can tease out the separate elements and start to take appropriate action. It is important to realise that this chart offers us a rough guide, its particular strength being its ability to offer a very wide and overall view. Clearly when there is a serious problem it will eventually require much more detailed examination.

As the book progresses we shall review not only some important spaces but also some of the biological, social and interpersonal systems and operate within them. In the next chapter we shall look at the home and the city, where the family system and our most intimate relationships operate. Then we shall look at the body as a space and review the systems of the brain altering its function to face danger and threat. We shall look at the way we respond to illness when the body space itself becomes unsafe. We shall review in some depth the most intimate interpersonal systems – between mother and child and between lovers. We shall look at the spaces in which these relationships occur and the way the relationships themselves modify those spaces. Finally we shall look at social systems, at friendship, work and wider social supports. In doing all this we shall try to look at us and our nature in a rather different way, emphasising not only systems and the safe spaces they need to operate but the very close interrelationships between different systems. To do this we shall bring together observations and ideas from a whole variety of different studies and disciplines, reminding ourselves that sometimes we cannot get what we need and that all too often we don't know what we need. It is hoped that by the end of the book we will have a better idea.

5

ALL SYSTEMS GO

When the first anatomists cut open the brain, they found within it some fluid-filled cavities whose roofs were laced with a mass of tiny intertwining blood vessels. They called these vessels the marvellous net, or in the Latin that they used, *Rete Mirabile*. They believed that within this net the human soul was literally ensnared. The ancient Hindus, by contrast, believed that a serpent lay coiled at the base of the spine, and that during the practice of Kundulani yoga and the experience of mystical states, this serpent rose up, eventually reaching the brain. In a whole variety of cultures, humours, energies and spirits moved in subtle ways through our every mysterious bodies. These models of the human being were sought not only to explain but also to justify. They helped us to find our place in the world and to justify our conduct.[1] The soul had to get to heaven, the serpents had to be raised, the energies had to be conserved and contained.

From the very start, we have endeavoured to link structure to function. How did the structure of the brain fit in with our idea of who we were and how we worked? When spirit and energy were central to the mechanics of person, it was these that featured in the explanation of brain function. In the twentieth century, spirit and energy remain but we now seek to link brain function not with them but with more concrete ideas involving information, adaptation, regulation and survival.

This book explores the importance of environment for a whole variety of human functions and the systems that sustain them. This ecological approach suggests that the space in which we are, or which we create, whether it be a material space or a personal space, will profoundly affect not only the way we feel and function, but also our mental and physical health.

In order to understand this relationship better, we shall now look in some detail at the brain and body mechanisms that translate personally appraised environmental conditions into bodily responses. To do this we must first define the key functional systems involved in all this – the brain, mind and body – and then look in some detail at the basic workings of the brain and its communications systems. In this way we shall understand how the brain influences and alters bodily activity.

If we were to start on the day of creation to design a human being, we might build in two basic modes: a safe space mode in which all was calm and relaxed and directed towards intimacy, conservation and consolidation, and a hostile space or alarm mode in which threat and danger could be faced and mastered. We shall see, as we progress, that these two modes do, in fact, exist and are mediated by a specialised part of the nervous system (the autonomic) and a variety of hormones. We shall see that safe space is not just a catchy title to a book, but is integral to the inbuilt responses of the brain.

Let us begin by taking a careful look at ourselves and the structures and systems involved in all this. Consider for a moment your bulk, your weight, the lie of your limbs, your posture, the beating of your heart, your breathing, your warmth. This is your body. Within it are heart, lungs, intestines, glands, blood vessels and so on. It is a delicate living system, only functions within ideal conditions and requires a constant supply of oxygen and sugar. Just as your mind and what you think is you, so your body and your organs are you.

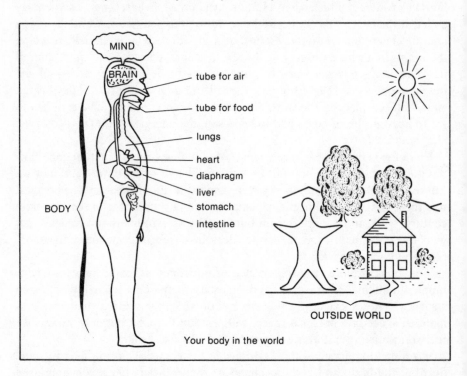

Your body in the world

Now without doing yourself any serious injury, let your head flop forward, then shake your head quite rapidly from side to side. You may be aware of a slight sense of movement within your skull. That is your *brain*. The brain is responsible for the physical processes necessary for mental function, rather in the way that the tube and transistors are necessary to produce a television picture. The brain not only gives rise to the content of mind in the form of our thoughts, ideas and so on, but also exercises a controlling influence over the internal state of the body, enabling it to adapt to external conditions.

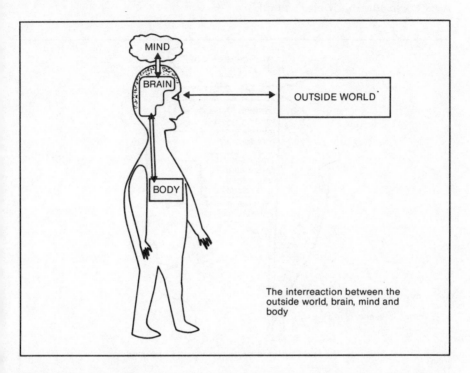

The interreaction between the outside world, brain, mind and body

If we are to understand our intimate relationship with our surroundings, we must give a little attention to the brain and, in particular, three major divisions. At the highest level is the information processor (cerebral hemispheres),[2,3] which receives input from our senses about the world, stores memory and gives rise to mind or consciousness. Immediately below this is the emotion generator (the limbic system),[4] which gives emotional value to perceptions and ideas developed in the information processor. At the lowest level is the bodily regulator (the hypothalamus and pituitary), which has hormonal and nervous connections to the body and regulates its activities. It is greatly under the influence of the emotion generator.

As you read this book you are conscious of this word and now the next one. This mental activity is a manifestation of your brain as an information processor.[5] Cut off the blood to the brain, as in a faint or strangulation, and the brain's metabolic function is impaired and consciousness of your mind is lost. Hence when we say 'he is unconscious', we might equally say he has no awareness of his mind's activity.

The dimension of mind is a special dimension in which concepts and ideas are interrelated and where action is initiated. Mind is personal, private and unique. You may share the world outside you with others, but the way that world registers in your mind will probably differ slightly from the way it registers in somebody else's mind.

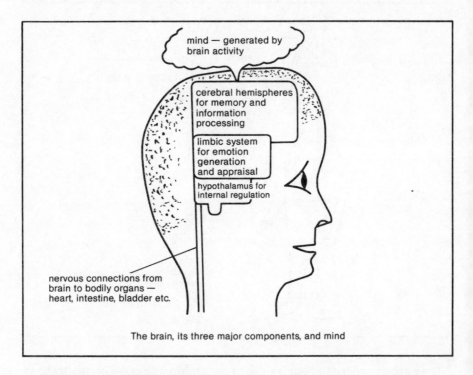

The brain, its three major components, and mind

As you are reading, you will be aware of the chair you are sitting on, the sky, the air temperature. This is all in the outside world which is all around us and within which we have to survive. What you do in that world can be described as your behaviour. While you are reading, your eyes are moving to follow this line of type, your head may be turning, your hands may be holding the book. Along with your more obvious behaviour, you are breathing, your heart is pumping and so on.

In this simple classification we have taken a 'giant leap' forward in our attempt to understand ourselves. Represented here is not only the whole of us, the whole person, but also the world in which that whole person lives. This approach will be followed through the book and is in marked contrast to generations of books involving self, understanding, insight, analysis and psychology, many of which dwell almost entirely on one part of the system to the exclusion of the others. They talk about you and me as if we were just minds with a vast collection of thoughts floating through space but with no

42

brain, no body, living nowhere in particular. According to this attitude, if you take care of the mind or soul, the inferior body will look after itself.

Here is the famous split of the Western intellectual tradition – the famous duality of Descartes, which saw the soul or mind as one reality and the body as another, rather inferior and unimportant reality. Long before Descartes, some of the more extreme ascetics had written off the body as the seat of sin and consigned it to rot at death, while the soul, the mind, the highest part of man, untainted by sexual desire or sin, went up to heaven. This tendency to emphasise the mind and ignore the body and brain still persists, partly out of habit and partly because it makes for easier reading and easier theory. It may be easy, but it is often misleading and is particularly inappropriate to today's world where we are becoming out of harmony, both with our bodies and the world in which we live.

Having identified these components, let us look at how they all work together and in close relationship with the outside world in even the simplest of activities. Consider what happens when, as you are reading this book, a friend arrives and offers you an ice cream. Outside in the real world is the ice cream. You respond to this through the central processor of your brain; your perceptions, thoughts, desires and intentions are experienced within your mind, which fills with longing, and you cannot wait to get your hands on the delicious morsel. In anticipation your body, stimulated by the bodily regulator, is already 'going wild', your stomach is churning, and digestive juices and saliva are flowing. Even in this most simple of examples, a true account of what is going on requires that all of you, the 'whole person', be looked at in relation to your environment.

To tell the story in more detail, we would need to make reference to your unique experience of all this and also to your capicity to exercise free will. In spite of the extreme temptation, you might choose not to have any ice cream, but to give all your attention to this book. In spite of your desires and the call of your body, you might say, 'Go to Hell, I don't want your sickly goo!' Here, in this simple example of whole person, are represented the complexities not only of mechanical or biological man (or woman) but also moral man (and moral woman).

In choosing to refuse the ice cream, we are of course exercising free will, choice and our rights as an individual to assess our own feelings and beliefs and act freely upon them. We are proud of this most human attribute, guard it jealously and protect it in codes of human rights and so on. We hold each other responsible for our actions and expect each other to face the consequences if we infringe certain codes.

Here we clearly see the three major contributors to any item of human activity. Firstly there is the basic biological structure of the brain and whole body which has been shaped by evolution and adaptation over millions of years. Secondly we see the changing external conditions present at that moment, and finally, most elusive, that transcendent and unique capacity of mind and individuality, to respond to past experience and present state through consciousness and to make personal choices.

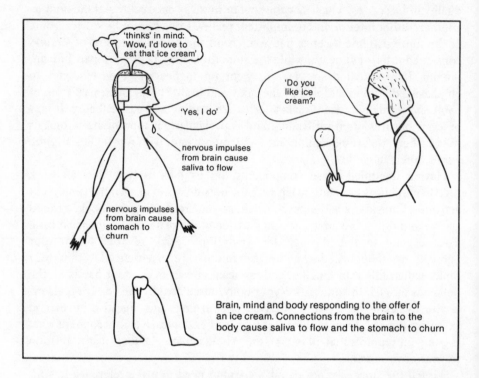

Brain, mind and body responding to the offer of an ice cream. Connections from the brain to the body cause saliva to flow and the stomach to churn

Darwin proclaimed survival of the fittest as a central evolutionary principle. The more successful animals would survive, produce more offspring and ensure the continuation of their genetic type. There has been a sinister extension of this argument. The individual is of secondary importance, a mere carrier or vehicle for the genetic material which shaped it, which it carries and which it will pass on through reproduction to another carrier. Safe space for the individual is a mere extension of a much more fundamental principle which we might call 'safe space for the gene'. This is said to explain such evolutionary curiosities as altruism. When a male zebra sacrifices himself, fighting a lion to protect his young or some of his troupe, it is clear that he will not survive and others like him may also not survive, but the young zebra, carrying the freshly shuffled and replicated genetic material, will and that's fine for the gene.

Of course, we have free will but that freedom, as we shall see, must be exercised against the constraints of a whole variety of inbuilt brain mechanisms that respond in a semi-automatic way to lack of safety and threat. We shall see later that the brave man or woman is one who defies their fear response, not one who has no fear response at all.

One simplified way of looking at some of the brain functions we are now going to describe is in terms of the capacity to ensure that, in the face of lack of safety, we maximise our capacity to adapt to ensure the survival of our genetic material.

If we are to take our understanding of safe space a stage further, we must now explore in more detail not only our conscious experience of threat to our safe space, but a series of complex and intricate brain-body mechanisms that are triggered off by threat. These involve the brain communicating with the body to alter its function. Just as the sight of the ice cream automatically causes bodily changes that will aid digestion, such as the flow of saliva and the churning of the stomach, so any obvious threat to safe space sets off its own series of dramatic bodily changes that will firstly prepare the body for fight or flight and, in the longer term, adapt it to stand up to prolonged stress.

The immediate alarm response involves the release of noradrenalin and adrenalin. The longer-term adaptation involves the release of steroid hormones. We shall describe these two brain-body systems as the adrenalin alarm response and the steroid adaptation response. Both these systems profoundly alter bodily function, but in rather different ways, and we shall explore them in some more detail.

After your brief introspection, you need to move now to a little role playing. You are a famous international secret agent (Jane or maybe James Bond) sitting comfortably in your luxurious hideaway. Body, brain, mind and the world are all at peace. Yet the mind[4] and brain are constantly ready to pick up any disruption or threat to this safe space and to respond. Suddenly, there is a terrible scream and the sound of smashing glass. At once the safety of the space is shattered, the quiet room becomes full of dangerous possibilities, for the noises suggest danger and threat, but to make it all worse, there is uncertainty about what's going on and what to do. Have the Russian secret agents finally arrived to take you away?

At once you are wide awake and alert, looking all around, listening. 'What's going on?' Images and ideas rush into the mind, you try to make sense of what is happening. Muscles are tense, pulse is racing, heart is pounding. There may be a sick feeling in the pit of the stomach, the palms are damp and the mouth dry. You may feel emotions of fear and anguish – is something terrible going to happen? There may be anger or rage, with fury directed against the intruders. The uncertainty and the possibility of danger have produced major changes in the body. The heart works harder, the blood is flooded with sugar, which is diverted from skin and gut to the brain and muscles where it is most needed. The blood clots more readily and the pupils dilate. The body is ready for 'fight or flight'. Here then is the state of alarm or emergency. In the wild, fragile and cold, with your animal skin covering your soft vulnerable body, these rapid bodily changes prepare you for action. You pick up your club, axe or sharp stone and go forth to battle, or maybe think better of it, grab your infant, cooking pot and the latest video and rush off into 'the wilds' to find a safe cave or tall tree.

These bodily changes are triggered off by the adrenalin alarm system. This system, known technically as the sympathetic adrenomedullary system, operates through the sympathetic nervous system, its own special nervous system, specifically designed to adapt the body to threat and to safe space. This inhibits digestive activity, speeds up metabolic activity and aids all processes that contribute to muscular efficiency. Its effect is rather like changing gear and depressing the gas pedal on a car.

It is particularly likely to be triggered by any acute threat to safe space,[6] such as loss of territory, status, food supplies, shelter or threat to person or loved one. This stimulates the emotion generator, which, acting through the internal regulator, triggers this system into responding, almost instantaneously, by using both direct nervous connections to most internal organs in the body, such as the heart, bowel, bladder and sexual organs, as well as the hormones, adrenalin and noradrenalin. In a predominantly fight-aggressive response, noradrenalin appears to be released, whereas in a flight-retreat response, adrenalin is the major hormone involved. The causal chain from external space to internal bodily space is clearly established, as in the link between outer social system and internal metabolic system.[7] A change in the social and personal spaces outside results in significant changes in bodily function.

Let us now take the drama a stage further. To do this you will need to involve yourself in a little more role playing. Let us imagine your worst fears are confirmed. The enemy secret service Dirty Tricks Brigade have arrived and are threatening to take you back to the capital of their country with them. The immediate alarm is over, but now you are faced with a more prolonged stress – you are being held against your will, and unless you escape (as Bond always does), you are going to have to make the long journey. Clearly your world has become unsafe and is going to remain so for some time to come.

Your brain starts to adapt the body to face this prolonged lack of safety. To do this its internal regulator makes use of its other main hormonal stress response system – the steroid hormonal stress response system. This is known technically as the hypothalamo-pituitary adrenocortical system.[8] This system alters the body's metabolic activity, particularly affecting salt, water and sugar metabolism, and ensures that extra sugar is available as fuel for hard working muscles and the nervous system. It lowers sexual drive and interest and, in the long term, can depress the activity of the body's immune system.[7] Although this system is always involved in prolonged adaptation to stress, it often comes into operation very shortly after the adrenalin alarm system, and is particularly likely to be triggered by emotions involved in group stability, male-female bonding and status within the hierarchy.[9]

During this stage of adaptation, you will be very 'keyed up'. You will sleep less. You will be much more vigilant. This stage of 'full alert' or 'all systems go' is, of course, very demanding and quite exhausting – everything is working 'flat out'. After a while in this state the body can no longer keep up with the demands and becomes unable to maintain its inner balance or equilibrium and begins to go wrong. You may feel exhausted, stressed, very nervous or even depressed. You may experience a variety of symptoms such as palpitations, stomach pains, loose bowels, aches and pains, and you may even become ill.

It is important to remember that the action of these two systems is initially adaptive. They ensure that the body is in a fit state to carry out the drastic action required to deal with the threat to safety. The snake in the grass or the charging buffalo is much better faced in a state of full alert with muscles tensed, well supplied with blood, sugar and oxygen.

During our review of these two extraordinary systems, we have not pursued the role of emotion in any great detail. Just as the brain adapts the body, so it has to label certain kinds of experience with a special quality that gives value and may impel action. We may look at a cornfield with a sense of calm and tranquillity, but our perception of the bull which emerges from behind the corn may vary and range from rage to terror, from anger to fear and all kinds of combinations of the two. To make matters more difficult, the relationship between emotion and these two hormonal systems is far from straightforward – but the importance of emotion as an indicator or a warning cannot be underestimated. Our emotions often say more about us in our world than words ever can.

It should not be forgotten that most of our alarm responses are effective and adaptive. We all talk about that shot of adrenalin which gives us that extra energy and concentration to get us through a sporting competition or a difficult interview. Often the challenge of the unsafe or the unknown can excite us and provoke us. Many will deliberately seek them out to enjoy the test and the triumph.

Although he originally trained as an architect, by the age of twenty-five Nick Mason was a world-famous drummer in 'Pink Floyd'. He loved his music, its performance, but one of his earliest passions was the motor car. While still with the band, he started to collect and to drive very fast cars. On a number of occasions he has driven at Le Mans at speeds exceeding 220 miles an hour. He has no doubts about the existence of his alarm response. Before a race he often feels queasy and while driving he is aware of extreme alertness and concentration which accompany the emotional arousal (both steroids and adrenalin actually alter mental function). On the race track he not only faces the technical challenge of the driving, but also, like photographer Don McCullin, finds he can face his own emotions and triumph over them. Racing conditions pose major threats but he uses all his skill and ingenuity to overcome them. He describes it as 'fighting your own battles in a precise and defined way, and enjoying the satisfaction of doing something well'. He derives much of his strength from being part of a team.

Charles Clark is a consultant neurologist at St Bartholomew's Hospital. His books on Everest are well known and he has made a number of assaults on the highest of all the peaks. Like Nick Mason, he finds the challenge demanding and enjoys overcoming the danger. He loves the feeling of triumph, of pitting himself against the demands of high and beautiful mountains. Like Nick Mason he too is well aware of his alarm systems and the way his body adapts to the extreme and prolonged stress of sub zero temperatures. He derives great strength from being part of a team and goes as far as to say, perhaps contrary to popular portrayal of those heroes in dramatised films of climbing, that 'ego is a killer . . . it's the expedition as a whole that's going to succeed . . . the whole is always bigger than the parts'. On the most difficult climbs in the most dangerous conditions, he gains great support and feelings of safety from the group. We shall see later how this support is protective in a whole variety of stresses and challenges.

Unfortunately many of the unsafe situations that provoke our autonomic arousal are not of our choosing. The threat is often insidious, ill-defined, and we have no way of either overcoming or avoiding it. It is this lack of safety sustained over time that is so damaging to our mental and physical health, and which all too frequently features in modern life. In these situations the bodily systems that were designed to protect us and to ensure our survival in unsafe spaces, start to damage the body themselves. We may not only experience symptoms, such as muscle aches, palpitations and digestive problems, but also a variety of unpleasant psychological changes, including poor sleep, irritability, anxiety and depression.

We can see the adverse effects of lack of safety repeatedly provoking an alarm response in the story of James W. He was a thirty-four-year-old insurance executive who had worked for most of his life in the same company. He had been promoted rapidly until he was twenty-seven but subsequently, although quite good at his job, received no further promotion. He was in charge of a small section of six people, dealing with renewal of insurance policies from overseas shipping companies. About two years previously, the company for whom he worked had been unexpectedly taken over by a much larger American multinational. The main management of the company was from New York and a number of quite dramatic changes were made. James W.'s small section was amalgamated with three other sections and a new, and younger man was put in above him as group general manager. Right from the start relations between them were poor and the standards that James had previously achieved now seemed to be unsatisfactory. At the end of each month, computer print-outs were reviewed by the group general manager, who maintained that the renewal and profit targets set by the directors in New York were not being reached. He urged James to adopt a more aggressive marketing stance and to encourage long-standing clients to increase their insurance cover, thus bringing in increased premiums and, it was hoped, greater profits.

James had established good personal relationships with a number of clients and found it difficult to adapt to the new approach required of him. He began to dread review meetings at the end of each month. For the few days prior to each meeting he found that his sleep was disturbed. He lost his appetite and his bowel function was altered. He started to suffer from diarrhoea and, particularly on the day before a meeting, from extremely unpleasant headaches. He began to take time off work, became irritable and short-tempered at home, and lost interest in many of his outside leisure activities.

He started to eat and drink more and put on weight. A routine insurance medical found his blood pressure raised compared with previous rather low readings. The company doctor warned him about this, which only increased his worry.

There are many physical causes for raised blood pressure, and it is often associated with changes in the walls of the arteries (atheroma). Kidney and hormonal disease often cause it, but in 80 to 90 per cent of cases no obvious physical cause can be found. In a proportion of these, life stress may play a major part (and James falls into this group) but a variety of other factors, including genetics, life-style, diet are also of major importance.

Let us look carefully at how a change of management, 3000 miles away in New York, contributed to the development of hypertension in James W. We can trace a chain of causality from loss of safe space in the outer world to disturbed function of the bodily system regulating the blood pressure.

Consider James' reactions in the period immediately preceding a profits review meeting with his new group manager. Faced with this meeting his information processor begins to make sense of it, using old memory stores and predictions of its outcome. This sense or meaning is unique to him and based on his personal past experience. In James' case, there were bad experiences with his rather stern and strict father and difficulties with his final exams at school. These he had to resit as his grades were not high enough to gain a place at the technical college where he wanted to study marine biology. (He did eventually take the degree but was then unable to find a job – so he reluctantly went into marine insurance.)

He was aware of all this information in consciousness, and tried to define choices and make decisions. Free will (what's left of it) featured here, but James could see no choices. He felt trapped and wronged and resentful. At the same time the part of the brain concerned with emotion (the emotion generator) was carrying out basic analysis of the incoming data, ascribing it simple value in terms of threat or physiological need. This manifested as anger towards the faceless directors in New York, and his new group manager, and fear over his failure and, even in the distance, the possible loss of his job.

The emotion generator was also triggering off bodily responses associated with these emotions, acting through the internal regulator via the sympathetic nerves, bringing about a release of adrenalin, noradrenalin and steroid hormones into the blood stream. As described earlier, the effect of this is to casue the heart to beat faster and harder, raising the blood pressure, the blood is drained from the digestive activities of the gut, producing feelings of nausea or even diarrhoea. This blood is diverted to the muscles for use in fighting or running away. Sugar is released from the stores of the liver to provide fuel and energy for all these exertions. The body is using all its primitive and semi-automatic responses to face a threat which is very hard to identify and which certainly requires a minimum of physical exertion.

It is just this sort of situation that repeated over time eventually leads to bodily damage. James' body is being repeatedly prepared for a battle that never happens, he begins to suffer chronic stress with a number of sustained bodily changes. At a physical examination his blood pressure was found to be 140/100 which, for a man of his age, was excessive. He started on medication to counter the effects of adrenalin and took beta-blockers to lower his blood pressure. At a review three months later, his blood pressure was still found to be high and the company doctor, suspecting some conflict at work, recommended that he seek help with a psychotherapist.

Bewildered by all this, James decided to comply and attended for weekly psychotherapy. The sessions were rather cold, formal and uninspiring, but it soon became clear to him that his therapist felt that James' difficulties in the company were related to his early childhood experiences. After twelve weeks, he was further demoralised and decided to terminate the therapy. The side effects of the blood pressure medication were upsetting his sex life and making him feel generally weak.

Concerned friends gave him the name of a doctor specialising in psychosomatic medicine and a holistic approach and James decided to consult him. After twelve weeks with this therapist, a number of important changes began to take place and three months later his blood pressure improved and his general attitude to work altered. He stopped all medication and eventually, after a further year without therapy, found a new job and made a new start. Three years on he remains well and without any further symptoms.

We shall now look more carefully at how the detailed description of James' problem was used by the psychosomatic doctor in therapy to produce beneficial changes.

It was clear that James' difficulties had to be seen in the context of his environment and, in particular, his uncertainty and conflict over his new position at work. Thus his high blood pressure was not simply a disease or a symptom to be treated on its own, but in this case could be seen as part of a whole person's response to an unsafe space. Understanding how James' nervous system transformed the threat and stress of work into a bodily response made this a lot easier. His emotion generator was triggering off noradrenalin release as part of the flight or fight response and this was, over a period of time, causing elevation of the blood pressure.

The therapist decided to work on a number of systems at once. He taught James to be aware of his bodily responses and to understand them. James confirmed that on the few days prior to review meetings, he could feel his heart pounding and noted that he had a dry mouth, cold extremities and sweaty palms in his attempts to counter these responses. The therapist taught him basic techniques of relaxation to use before and during periods of stress. Relaxation techniques work in a number of ways. There is an element of relearning – teaching the brain not to set its alarm system off so readily. James was encouraged to face the idea of review meetings in a calm and relaxed frame of mind, to sit quietly and peacefully and see if he could think about them without becoming too emotional.

Another part of the effectiveness of relaxation techniques involves reversing or limiting the alarm response once it has been set off. James was encouraged to pick up any signs of this – pounding heart, sweaty palms and so on – and instead of responding with more fear and despair to feelings he couldn't understand, he was taught to understand their origins and to seek to control, and eventually diminish them using relaxation. Although this worked for James, it must be emphasised that many people with high blood pressure need something more than relaxation or change of life-style. However, a proportion of sufferers will be helped by these methods, especially in the early stages.

Gradually his body's automatic stress response was modified. The therapist also helped him to try to view the threat of work in a somewhat new light. This involved altering what was going on in his mind. He made some reference to James' early experiences and looked once again at what James saw as the apparently disastrous and irreversible consequences of failure. James began to see that there was life outside the office and that, although jobs were difficult to get, he was highly qualified. Possibly, by taking some small drop in salary, he could find himself new employment. Finally, the therapist capitalised on this last option, encouraging him to look in the long term at altering his work situation – by finding a new job. This combination of measures produced the improvement already described and seems to have been generally successful.

Now it is not the intention in this book to paint human beings as timid, cowering little creatures who cannot deal with unsafe spaces or who run from danger at the slightest provocation. In the face of threat or adversity, we can show great courage, resolve and determination. As the examples at the start of the chapter show, we often cope well with threats, we can recognise them, see where we can choose freely from a variety of options, respond effectively and discover where, in doing all this, we can utilise a whole range of talents and skills.

James' alarm response derived in the first instance from real threat in the outer material space. This makes it very similar to a whole class of stress and fear responses that are triggered by real provocation in the real material world. The breaking glass described earlier, the threat of a violent attack as in a mugging or an attack by a wild animal, are all good examples of this. It is these kinds of things that we have had to face since we and our animal cousins first started living on this planet.

In order to understand in a little more detail how crude physical disruptions of safe space affect us, we shall now explore the anatomy of one particular emotional response – the fear response – and show how for each person their particular fear response may be linked with various combinations of respone in mind, brain or body.[10]

Fear involves three components: subjective feelings of fear; the mental element that we experience when afraid; apprehension, feeling jittery, feeling unpleasant and so on. Along with this mental or subjective component of fear, there are the physiological changes of fear.[11] These have been described in some detail earlier in the chapter and are of course initiated by the emotion generator and the internal regulator acting through the sympathetic and parasympathetic nervous systems. These changes include racing of the heart, dryness of the mouth, muscle tension, feelings of emptiness in the stomach and so on. The third component is the behaviour that is associated with or follows on from these other two elements. This often takes the form of an escape response, a wish to run away, but in trying to neutralise the source of the fear we may also respond with action that involves some kind of aggressive attack.

For some people aggression and fear are very closely linked and for such people, threat may be met with fairly instant aggression. At times this aggression is adaptive – as in warfare – but in domestic situations it can cause serious damage. In different people fear may express itself in different ways: thus one person when afraid may experience racing of the heart but very little subjective feeling of fear, whereas another person may experience extreme muscle tension and subjective feelings of fear but not much else. The situation is further complicated by observations on treatment which suggest that when fears are treated as, say, in a phobic disorder, one dimension of the fear may dramatically alter but not the other, but in spite of this the patient may well report an improvement. Thus a course of relaxation therapy may allow a fearful patient to experience fear without so much increase in heart beat, and even if other elements of fear may remain the same, the patient will report improvement.[11]

This three component model of fear does allow us to define bravery easily.[10] Bravery is the capacity to resist escaping, screaming or submitting to some other piece of basic behaviour in the presence of subjective feelings of fear and physiological changes of fear. The brave person is not someone who feels no fear at all but someone who, when in a state of fear, is able to overcome or resist the urge to escape and engage in constructive action of even aggression.[10]

The range of fear that people show in response to a given situation or stimulus is vast. If a mouse were to run across the floor of a crowded room, a large number of people might feel this tiny mouse to be a threat to their safety, scream out or try to escape. Someone, however, would take great pleasure in showing off to the others in the room how she or he was able to bend down, pick up the poor mouse, by now feeling far more unsafe than anybody in the room, and remove it.

The reasons for this variability are not well explained. Fears certainly have a constitutional element, and it is possible to breed very fearful and less fearful strains of mice. Certain specific fears are also innate. Baby chimpanzees are fearful of snakes or the severed head of another chimpanzee even when they have never ever seen either of them before. Likewise children, as they develop, exhibit a whole variety of fears. These include dogs, heights, the dark and so on. They change in severity fairly constantly with age. As well as innate fears there are various ways in which fears can be acquired. A single frightening experience with fire or violence or whatever may induce prolonged and severe fears, and similarly repeated exposure to mildly fearful situations can produce similar effects. Fear in other people can cause us to be afraid and information about the danger of something can also induce fear. All these feelings of fear are aggravated by the feeling that we can do nothing to influence or control the fear. Fear then is like so many of our feelings. It can only really be understood by looking at our whole self in a real and well-defined environment which has particular meaning to us and to which we can respond in particular ways.

Fear and anxiety are first and foremost a warning. They are feelings that tell us something is wrong in the outside world. When we experience these feelings, we need to look outside and ask what has upset our safety. What is the threat or the danger? Unfortunately, we have all become so accustomed to thinking of fear and anxiety as a symptom, as an indicator of neurosis, mental illness or personal weakness, that when we experience such feelings, instead of looking at our world and what is going on in it, we rush to the doctor or the therapist or the counsellor. In fact the anxiety may be telling us something very important about our lives, just as a feeling of pain in our finger would tell us that our finger is being burnt. First of all we must always look most carefully at what is going on in the world and the spaces around us, and what that means to us.

If there is no threat or danger outside in the material world and we still feel fear, then clearly there is some kind of false alarm and we need to ask what is going on. Why the false alarm? In such a situation there may be something wrong with the mechanism. The brain or the body may not be working properly and may be registering feelings of fear when there is nothing to be afraid of. This happens in a variety of medical conditions, which include thyroid disease and anaemia, certain heart irregularities, angina and a number of other, hormonal diseases. In such instances, full medical investigations will reveal the cause of the fear and it usually disappears with appropriate treatment. Fear may also occur because our appraisal is inaccurate and is grossly exaggerating the degree of threat that is present.

For James, there was some degree of real threat in the external material space around him, although his perception of that threat and his inability to take constructive action greatly aggravated its effect. Many of the things that we fear in the outside world are not well defined and solid. Like big black spiders or little white mice, they are much more subtle. They derive, to a large degree, from our own perception of the world. They involve ideas that we impose upon the world, that make it feel unsafe and threatening where it otherwise might not be so. We might label this kind of threat of danger 'imposed' – imposed because we ourselves impose it on the world. Some people also call this sort of threat or danger 'neurotic'. The fear and the anxiety resulting from this can cause a great deal of discomfort and unhappiness, not least because we often feel helpless in the face of these fears, not really understanding their origin or not being able to do much about them. This kind of fear often features in a variety of psychiatric conditions including anxiety states, some kinds of depression and phobias. Let us look at how you can begin to diminish these imposed fears in yourself – if they are present.

It will now be clear that an apparent lack of safety and our fear response to that can, to a large degree, be related not to what is really happening in the world but to our view of the world. It follows on logically from this that if we can change the way we view the world, change the way we think about it, then we may perceive it as it really is – that is, as safe – and we may experience less fear or no fear at all. All this sounds like common sense and to a large extent it is. Many of us, when in difficulties or when feeling demoralised, might say to ourselves something reassuring like 'Come on, pull yourself together – it's nothing really'. If we can alter the way the highest unit processes information then, in the absence of any serious real external threat, we may be able to abolish those irrational or imposed fears.

Jane D. became quite successful in local politics but found herself feeling increasingly unsafe when she spoke in public. She had always been rather sensitive about any public performance, and during a school prizegiving at the age of eleven she had seen a teacher vomit and then collapse on the stage. Recently she had been feeling not only fearful in public, but sick too, and had noticed her heart beating excessively (palpitations). She found that even the thought of having to talk in a group produced severe anxiety with fearful thoughts and worry about her bodily state, its palpitations and sickness. She also experienced a sense of shame and withdrawal and was getting depressed about all this. It was clear that she needed to change the way she thought about public speaking, and to change the way her emotion generator responded to the situation.

Like many shy people, when she was confronted by a group of people she responded as if she were confronted by some sort of serious danger. Her emotion generator had learned to recognise any group of more than two or three people as a danger. This was associated with a variety of physical alarm signals which involve, as you may recall, the release of adrenalin, steroids and various nervous impulses relayed through the sympathetic nervous system, producing feelings such as sickness and palpitations. These feelings in turn are recognised as further evidence of fear and cause more distress and a wish to retreat and escape.

In the face of this, the subject Jane wondered what was going on and secondly, sought to take some action – what was to be done about this danger? In many shy people there is often some feeling of wanting to run out of the room, hide, scream or escape. Here then is the initial picture: it is a familiar picture to many people and covers a variety of rather irrational anxieties or fears. For some people, going in an aeroplane may trigger off these feelings; for others, sitting an examination; for others, simply worrying about some conflict at work or some minor failure will also produce these problems. Here then is the initial analysis of the problem, here also is a clear statement of how the mental and physical elements of the response to unsafe space are inextricably mixed.

Let us extend this a little now to see how the physical elements of fear, in particular, distort the situation and how the subject (Jane D.) goes on to tell herself further misleading things about the situation in which she finds herself. Thus in a state of fear the subject is hardly concerned with what is going on in the outside world but is completely preoccupied with the very unpleasant feelings in her body. She feels sick, she feels that she might actually vomit in public, she has palpitations, and as her heart pounds she worries whether she is going to faint or whether, in fact, her heart might stop and she will have a heart attack. Thus, the information processor, which is asking the question – what is going on? – is somewhat bewildered when confronted with the palpitations and the sickness.

In answer to the question 'What is going on?' the information processor cannot really produce an answer except to say 'something is wrong with my heart and something is wrong with my stomach'. In response to the urge for action, the central processor can only come up with the idea that 'I am going to make a fool of myself and I can't do anything'. The subject therefore not only has to deal with fear of people, but also worries about the heart and the inability to do anything.

It is becoming clear that a vicious circle has been set up. Worries about the heart and being sick are now very much centre stage and the subject's perception is of a new danger – 'Am I going to be sick in public or am I going to have a heart attack?' The emotion generator now sounds off a further mental alarm, and the internal regulator releases more hormones and sends off more nervous messages which have the effect of increasing the feeling of sickness and worsening the palpitations. This, in turn, presents the information processor with new perceptions of bad heart and sickness. The subject is now quite unable to do anything, and simply worries about the danger, the sickness and the possibility of a heart attack. Here then is a classic cycle in which what might seem to be a fairly moderate and manageable threat becomes extremely dangerous and disabling.

A treatment plan

Clearly this is a complex and intricate problem, but there are a number of ways in which it may be approached. These approaches involve telling yourself a new story about what is going on in the outside world and also identifying what is going on in your body in a new and perhaps more constructive way. This, in turn, will let you understand the basis for your feelings and will give you some mastery over yourself. What seems to be a sea of fear and panic, what seems to be a return to the helpless state of infancy, can be made amenable to adult coping, and what seems to be completely unsafe can begin to become safe again. Let us take this one point at a time, using a generally applicable approach of the kind that helped Jane.

Look again at what is going on in the world and try to see it in a new way. Instead of immediately identifying three people as a crowd, as a signal for danger, try to see them as what they are, rather than what you impose upon them. Try to say different things to yourself about them – they are nice, nasty, supportive, kind or whatever. How might you respond to them in a different way? Once you start to see them differently, then your feelings of fear might seem to be somewhat inappropriate. Nevertheless, some kinds of fear may still persist for a while. It is very important that you identify these and make sense of them and don't get carried away with them. You also need to set about trying to identify and label your bodily responses in a way that makes more sense to you. My heart is beating fast because I feel slightly afraid; this is not sign of a heart attack, this is normal response to fear. Similarly, the feelings of sickness do not mean that I am about to vomit, but are again a further signal of danger. Label your fear responses in a way that allows you to get control of them. Finally, the central processor or central computer is asking for some sort of action – what is to be done about this problem? Instead of panicking or trying to run away, see if you can learn to say helpful things, both to yourself and others, which will diminish the feelings of fear and anxiety. Perhaps learn to share it with friends, have a few items of conversation written on your sleeve or written on a piece of paper. You can always talk about the weather or politics or something like that and probably get some kind of reasonable response. All this sort of thing is bound to help. It is a beginning, it is a key, it shows you that even though the world may feel very unsafe and threatening, the threat and lack of safety can be broken down into components, that there is some sense to it and that you can begin to interfere with it.

For Jane D. what was a global feeling of panic and fear, a complete lack of safety, began to break down into parts. She began to separate the situation itself and the things she thought about the situation from her bodily responses and the things she thought about them. Gradually this ability to organise what was originally a general panic began to give her some confidence, and working initially with only small groups she was able to start with seminars and evenually move on to lectures and public meetings. She still gets a slight feeling of nausea sometimes, or a fast pulse, but she expects it now and when it happens she begins to feel safe with it, rather than as if she were about to die.

The chemical control of fear

This review would not be complete without some brief reference to the chemical control of fear. If what we fear is related to threats to our safe space in the real world, its appreciation and its effects will depend on the efficient functioning of the brain and its emotion centre. If we interfere with the function of this, we can suppress or even abolish the feelings of fear. This can be done with a whole variety of drugs which include such old and natural remedies as opium or alcohol or some of the more modern synthetic substances such as tranquillisers of the 'valium' family – the benzodiazepines.

It is estimated that between nine and ten per cent of all people living in the United Kingdom experience at least one month of anxiety every year. In attempting to deal with this anxiety they were prescribed, in 1980, around nineteen million prescriptions for sedatives and tranquillisers and thirteen and a half million prescriptions for hypnotics.[12] As well as that, they consumed a fair amount of alcohol. Although there are many reasons for drinking alcohol, a very important one is to do with alcohol's capacity to eliminate feelings of fear and anxiety. Alcohol is frequently used in war time as a standard ration to sailors and is extremely effective at eliminating fear, hence the old expression 'Dutch courage'. In the United Kingdom in 1983 [13] 916,000 hectolitres of spirit were consumed, 62,000 hectolitres of beers and 5,359 hectolitres of wine – a sizeable intake. Surveys in the United States estimate that 70% of the adult population consume 300 million gallons every year. As in the United Kingdom, this leads to very high levels of alcohol related illness – perhaps as many as 250,000 deaths a year in the United States alone.

It may seem strange that alcohol is so closely linked with social activity, but we should not forget that although the love, support and friendship of people are a vital component of our safe space, the possibility of being excluded or rejected is often present and this can be associated with considerable fear. This can usually be abolished by a pint of beer or a glass of whisky. All this is well recognised by the advertisers, who invariably feature supremely confident, socially competent charmers, exuding bonhomie in crowded pubs or parties, at home both with a gang of men or with the girl of their choice. There is never a hint of shyness or insecurity – that doesn't feature in our view of ourselves – and if it does, you can buy your way out of it, with alcohol of course.

57

Although there are many reasons for drinking, undoubtedly a very important one is lack of safety in the environment. It is generally agreed that the sharp rise in alcoholism in the UK during the Industrial Revolution was related to the very unpleasant and unsafe living conditions of the new generation of workers crammed into the rows of faceless back-to-back houses. The steady and continuous rise in alcohol and drug consumption in modern industrial society perhaps tells us something rather important about the space around us, and our capacity to do something about it.

In this chapter we have traced that complex chain of causality, in which our extraordinary brain not only identifies lack of safety in the outside world and presents us with data allowing conscious choices, but at the same time drastically alters bodily function in ways that may be adaptive as well as life-saving. The stress response system is of central importance in our body's ability to cope with hostile and threatening circumstances and we should not be too afraid or unduly concerned about short term responses of this kind, though we should always try to understand them.

We have seen too how these apparently adaptive changes may also eventually produce a wide variety of mental and physical symptoms and even disease. Understanding exactly how these stress responses work gives us a much better chance to pick up inappropriate or damaging responses and to do something about them. The response that in one situation can be adaptive and life-saving can, in another, be maladaptive and damaging.

A central decision in assessing all this must relate to the environment. Is there a 'real' threat to our safety and if so what is the best action to take? If there is no significant real threat, then why are we responding in this way and what action can we take to understand and modify our responses? Bodily feelings are not just about adaptation, they can also be seen either as a warning about something going wrong in the outside world, or as an indication that something is wrong in the way we perceive or adjust to the outside world.

We all need safe space and we should attend to our responses when that safety is threatened. We can learn much about ourselves and our relationships with the world if we are honest. If the job or the neighbours or the family are provoking even a moderately severe alarm response, then try to identify the threat and try to take some action. If there really is nothing out there that is significantly threatening, then look within. The inner roots of inappropriate alarm responses often go back many years to long-forgotten experiences, something in childhood. In the second part of the book we shall pay particular attention to these.

Remember too that when you are faced with excess of inappropriate alarm, a whole lot of activities can help to diminish the arousal it causes. Understanding it and analysing it, standing back from it, sharing it with others, especially those you love or those in a similar position. Sport, especially swimming or gentle jogging, can also combat it and the cultivation of relaxation, meditation and therapeutic or intimate touch also helps. As well as your mind it's your body that's responding, and knowing it better can give you all kinds of new ways of listening to it, being with it and modifying how it responds.

6

SURVIVING IN THE CITY

The first human creatures quite like us have only been on the earth for three million years. These creatures stood on two legs, were shorter than us and had brains about the size of a grapefruit (400 cubic centimetres). Over two and three quarter million years the size of that brain trebled to the size of a small melon. Our own species, that of homo sapiens, the large-brained hominid, has been on the earth a mere two hundred and fifty thousand years. The development of agriculture only occurred in the last ten thousand years and, later still, writing and written culture. Civilisation and its elaborate social organisation occupies the tiniest fraction of time in our evolutionary progress. We are really just beginners when seen against the timescale of the planet's development.

This earth, the planet where we must all find safe space, came into existence some four thousand, five hundred million years ago. Perhaps a thousand million years later, the first vestiges of life began to appear and by three thousand million years ago the first multicellular living things had begun to appear. It was not until six hundred million years ago, a period known as the Cambrian explosion, that there began to be a proliferation of life forms, but the first mammals did not appear until about sixty-five million years ago.

The small brains of our early ancestors did not prevent some quite impressive social and technical activity, often associated with the pursuit of safe space. At the DK site in Tanzania, a circle of rocks defining territory and providing some shelter for communal eating is thought to date back nearly two million years. In China, fossils of homo erectus half a million years old have been found in caves, and the first definite evidence of fire for cooking dates back three hundred and fifty thousand years.[1] One hundred thousand years ago, Neanderthal man was making use of fire and clothing to protect him against the inhospitable climate, and using stone tools for hunting and for working upon his immediate environment and for use in hunting.[2]

We can get some idea of what life might have been like, about one hundred thousand years ago, by looking at the way the Australian Aborigines lived. They were cut off from the rest of the world at the end of the last Ice Age, some ten thousand years ago.[3] They were nomadic and lived in small groups of four to six families. Their main source of food was derived from hunting, which was carried out by small groups of men, whilst the women looked after the children. The conditions in which they lived, and successfully survived, were not exactly sustaining or safe. Nevertheless, their extreme ingenuity, perseverance, dexterity and spirit ensured that they survived, generally found enough food to eat, and even managed to involve themselves in leisure and pleasure. They enjoyed dancing and singing and decorating themselves. The Aborigines of Australia, like the bush men of the Kalahari, were formidable hunters. The bush men could hit a moving animal with a bow and arrow at one hundred and fifty yards.[4] They were also able to construct traps and did so both on land and in water with very considerable skill. They had a vast and intricate knowledge of animal behaviour and the habits of animals and were, of course, absolutely wedded to the environment in which they lived. For all that, they were not touched by a revolution which affected the rest of mankind and which has considerable implications for our understanding of safe space. That revolution we may quite simply refer to as farming.

This change from being hunter-gatherers roaming in small bands to a more stable and settled relationship with the land seems to have occurred as recently as ten to fifteen thousand years ago. Most authorities suggest that it occurred simultaneously at a variety of locations that were favourable to human habitation. The deltas of large rivers, such as the Tigris, the Euphrates and the Indus, may have been centres of early agricultural activity.[3] With the advent of agriculture, territory took on a completely new significance, and geographical stability allowed man to develop for the first time a much more intricate relationship with his surroundings. Not only could he start to build secure homes, but he could also decorate them, construct idols and totems and hoard beautiful objects. Although caves had been decorated long before this, it is only with the stability born of agriculture that art really began to develop. The accumulation of food surpluses freed some members of society from hunting and food production, and allowed specialisation. Whilst some committed themselves to the production of food, others could involve themselves in building, decoration, art and so on. Thus, with farming the whole edifice of civilisation, as we know it today, began its ponderous journey.

We may think of the early human hunters relying on aggression and physical force as the mainstays of their survival. The human farmer, by contrast, would require a less aggressive approach, being committed to territory, to intricate family and communal links, to involvement with agriculture, and having close and much more sensitive relationships with animals. Although some of these ideas may have passed through learning from one generation to the next, a significant part of them probably derived from our genetic heritage. That heritage is with us today and seeks expression still in much of our behaviour.

Throughout the world there are similar patterns of family and domestic structure. In the nuclear family this involves close personal bonds between a core man and woman, with kinsmen, perhaps other spouses, and related members of the older generation also being involved. A common variant of the nuclear family is the stem family, in which only one child remains at home bringing his spouse and children into the family, thus allowing the land and property to be maintained, and not exhausted by excessive demands. In this situation there is a variety of cultural mechanisms that eventually lead to the other family members leaving home to find new territory for themselves. Even with specialisation in technology and science, most people still grow plants and keep pets – no doubt remnants of our agricultural heritage – and many of the rich buy houses or even farms in the country, seeking to 'get back to the land'.

It seems we are now in yet another transition, perhaps culturally determined, in which agricultural man, with all his older more basic needs, is being replaced by urban man, as an increasingly large proportion of the world's population lives in cities. For all their obvious economic and cultural purposes, cities cannot survive if they do not provide certain basic life support systems, safeties and amenities for those who live in them. We are now witnessing in many large and important cities erosion of these basic human requirements, with a variety of serious consequences. Sex, drugs and rock 'n' roll have replaced bread and circuses, and it's no longer just the gladiators who get sacrificed.[5] There is too much technology spewing out everything from pollution to high energy radiation, with too many people competing for too few highly priced resources.[6] The city, this man-made material environment, is rapidly becoming the dominant physical and social environment in the West and in the Pacific Basin. Cities are extraordinary and exciting places and allow a vast degree of specialisation. Many of us living in cities are there because we chose to be. We are there for a whole variety of benefits, but it is becoming increasingly clear that these are being obtained at a considerable cost, and that in a whole variety of ways cities are becoming unfit places for human habitation.

The urban planners have laid out their grand avenues, fine parks and industrial estates. They have put up buildings that touch the clouds and tunnels that go deep under the ground. They have driven motorways over the roof-tops and criss-crossed the great rivers with bridges and walkways, yet somewhere along the way the individual human being and her or his safe spaces have been forgotten. We all know that cities live on electricity, exhaust gas, neon, money, steel and living people. Let us remind ourselves of what the people live on and the nature of the spaces that they require – which of course is why they create the cities in the first place. Cities, by their nature, are crowded places, but this does not suit people.

Crowding not only affects liability to mental and physical illness, but also correlates dramatically with social pathology, and crime in particular. Urban overcrowding is particularly relevant to the United Kingdom. If England and

Wales are considered together as a country, then they become the third most densely populated country in the world – third after Bangladesh and Taiwan. In fact, 80% of the population of the United Kingdom live in towns, with 13% in Greater London.[6]

In the United States the crime rate is three times higher in cities with more than one million inhabitants than it is in rural areas. In France the incidence of violent crime is closely related to the size of the town.[7] These studies have been replicated in both the United Kingdom and the United States. There the FBI Index shows that crime per 100,000 people increases from 2229 for rural areas to 7629 for cities with a population of more than one million. Causes for this are hard to identify, but the speed and size of the city, anonymity, break-up of communities, overcrowding and confinement of large numbers of disadvantaged people in one place all contribute.[8]

Studies of delinquency also show a correlation between large cities and overcrowding. Once again, causal factors are far from clear.[9] For example, a particular feature in the United Kingdom is the persistence of delinquent sub-cultures suggesting that a delinquent tendency passes down through families as learned behaviour. Support for this is found in studies which suggest that certain schools actually seem to encourage delinquent behaviour[10] In Liverpool the rate of theft has been closely related to a variety of indices, which include social deprivation and a profound and widespread lack of safety in many aspects of the environment, as indicated by the presence of job instability, unemployment, school absenteeism, violent crime and illegitimacy.[11]

Although people feel degraded and defiled by theft, it is violent crime that is most disruptive, intrusive and dramatic of all the inner city problems. In London now, 50 percent of women fear violent attack, rape or assault and many are afraid to travel on public transport. Many old people will not go out and parents are afraid to let their children go out. In New York, the situation is much more serious and violence is among the most common causes of death for black males between the ages of eighteen and twenty-five.

The presence of unsupportive and unsafe conditions in the immediate surroundings has profound psychological and physical consequences and has its most direct effects on the least privileged members of a city. Unskilled manual workers [12] make up the bulk of those living in inner cities. When compared with professional and managerial staff, they have a higher rate of mental illness, six times the number of accidents, double the incidence of deafness, and infant mortality is two and a half times higher. This is reflected in a close correlation between cause of death and both [13] the degree of overcrowding and overall population density. In the United Kingdom, the health gap between rich and poor continues to widen.[14] New studies in a number of countries show that things are often even worse for the unemployed[15]. Inner city conditions not only contribute to physical illness but also to mental illness. This is partly due to the general lack of a safe, supportive environment, and to the tendency of people to drift to deprived areas after chronic mental illness.

People from the more privileged parts of society who suffer serious mental disorder, such as schizophrenia,[16] drug addiction or alcoholism, often lose their jobs and their homes, and may be deserted by their families. They then 'drift' to the poorest parts of the city, and form the ranks of the homeless, who have no friends or family to take any interest in them or care for them. In socio-medical 'new speak' these people are known as the homeless and rootless. They suffer from increased rates of serious mental illness, alcoholism, epilepsy and TB.[17] In a number of countries the closure of large mental hospitals may well swell their numbers considerably[18].

Yet the hardest of people in the toughest of cities still remain human. We cannot fully deny that heritage. The soft underbelly still has to be protected or fed. The breat still needs an infant to suckle. The hardest man longs for the soft touch of another human being, and at night when all the screens stop flashing and the last video cassette has finally come to an end, the illusion of electronics and imagination must give way to aching limbs, tired eyes, weariness and sleep. Even the high of dextroamphetamines seldom runs much more than thirty-six hours and after that it's bedtime. The wildest men and women are all at once like children and slipping out of their shining, clinging, crotch-hugging disco gear and, vulnerable and naked in their skin, they will go home to a soft bed in a safe place, perhaps with somebody to cuddle, and lie down and fall deeply asleep. There's no place like home! All cities, of course, comprise hundreds of thousands of individual homes. Here, allowing for the diversity of culture, we find an extraordinary uniformity in our personal need for safe space and the material form it takes.

Quite rapidly, we can develop a rather personal affection for even the simplest home of our own. Many of us will find in a small flat or a room a character and a feeling that gives us a sense of belonging, of possession, a sense of 'being at home'. Imagine your first home away from your parental home. Perhaps it is a very simple and basic place, but put a few pictures on the wall, bring a few favourite books and a rug for the floor, put your clothes in the cupboard and then eat or drink something in the place, and quite soon it begins to feel safe, a place to come home to, a place where you belong. A place where you can go to sleep.

If cities are to provide safe spaces for human beings, they must fulfil our requirements for territory, privacy and personal space. We need to control the territory that we occupy (territorial rights), and to be able to regulate our social contact with other people (privacy) and the intimacy to which our body is subjected (personal space).

As most higher animals need territory, so do we humans.[19] This needs to be secure and constant and respected by those around us. Territory includes home, garden and the areas immediately surrounding our home. The territorial behaviour of animals perhaps expresses a basic need for safe space. A whole variety of creatures, from sticklebacks to lions, from chickens to cats, from blackbirds to eagles, identify or mark out a piece of land, air or water, which they regard as their own and which they will defend, in some cases with extreme ferocity. An adult male bird is usually undefeatable by birds of his own species when standing at the centre of his territory.[20]

Within the safe space of this defined piece of territory the animal will have access to food, shelter, a space for sexual display and an area in which the young may grow up with a fair degree of safety. Within such a territory birds will, of course, build their nests. The behaviour of animals in relation to their territory shows an extraordinary degree of uniformity and has been studied in enormous detail over the last twenty to thirty years. Aggression is closely related to territory and the strategies used by animals show a fascinating degree of variation. Perhaps most dramatic are the well-known contrasts between hawks and doves. In defence of their territory hawks will fight fiercely with other hawks until one animal is seriously injured and then retreats. The doves, by contrast, seldom fight, although they display extravagantly as if about to fight, but eventually one of them will always retreat rather than fight.

If there is any doubt about the degree to which the animal origins of territorial defence have intruded into our culture, then we should look carefully at an important defence to homicide under English law. This states that in defence of his house, the owner or his family may kill a trespasser who would forcibly dispossess them of that house or property, just as they might kill in self-defence a man who attacks them personally. The home is our most important piece of territory and later in the chapter we shall review this in a little more detail. But first of all let us look at what might be regarded as our universal human requirements for privacy and space.

The body itself and the area around the body is regarded as owned or personal and intruders into that area are regarded as threatening and may provoke anxiety.[21,22] In certain situations, such as travelling on the underground, subway or rapid transit, these intrusions are unavoidable. Here we take steps to shut out the unwanted encounter, avoiding eye contact, body contact and so on. One important function of this personal space is to keep stimulation at an optimum level and to avoid excessive sensory input which in itself may be damaging and bad for health as well as threatening to our sense of safety and security. Our need to be alone and enjoy privacy is a further expression of this and an essential requirement of the immediate environment. We need varying amounts of privacy, which we can control and regulate. Too much contact with other people can be extremely stressful. Children, in particular, are adversely affected without periods of reduced stimulation.

The space immediately around our body we may identify as intimate space. Into this space we will only allow those whom we love deeply – children, co-habitees, sexual partner, and our very closest friends whom we may embrace or cuddle. At parties, when dancing, or on very special occasions, we may allow others into this very intimate one. An intrusion into this zone which is not invited will produce a high degree of anxiety and concern, and may arouse the flight and fight system. Many people will respond to such intrusion with violence or aggression. In some situations even eye contact may result in an aggressive outburst. Hence the expression 'eye-balling', which is particularly resented in such situation as clubs, bars, pubs and so on.[23]

Contact with the surfaces of our body is also carefully regulated and access to that surface is controlled by well-defined social conventions. There are strict rules that govern who may touch us and where they may touch us, and males and females show quite distinct patterns with regard to where they may be touched by their mothers and fathers.

Beyond the intimate is the personal space. This extends to about three or four feet beyond our body surface. We generally feel comfortable making social contact with people who stand at the edge of this space. When talking to strangers, however, or people we have not met before, we *will* notice that a much larger distance is preferred. This is known as the social zone. For even more casual contacts, we may consider a public zone which involves placing a distance of about ten feet between us and a stranger.[24]

The exact size of these spaces is closely related to culture and those from the town will tend to be more at ease standing closer to other people than those from the country. Arab men tend to stand much closer to each other when talking than, say, men from England or the United States. Americans in general seem to stand slightly closer to each other than people from the United Kingdom. Italian men are quite likely to touch each other when talking, whereas in the United Kingdom, particularly, this sort of thing is generally not acceptable.

Society enshrines these basic needs into a whole range of conventions and laws. The material expression of this, of course, involves designing homes and streets and cities that respect these fundamental human requirements. The most immediate facilitator of all this is, of course, our own individual home and the space around it. Within this material structure our intimate and territorial needs have to be fulfilled.[25] Failure to appreciate this seems to have produced disastrous results.

For a long time we have not adequately considered our own ecology and the nature of the space that we need in order to survive. For more than fifty years we have been building high-rise and high-density houses with utter disregard for people's basic nature and needs. Politicians praising these extraordinary structures point proudly to statistics showing how they and their party have rehoused more of the population than any previous administration. These inhumane 'prisons' express the worst features of social expediency and a bureaucracy that make absurd assumption about the way we are. The buildings deny and ignore our true nature, and were in the main created by people who gave as little thought to the social and personal consequences of their structures as the early industrial revolution architects gave to the health and hygiene consequences of their structures.[26] In place of food poisoning, malnutrition and tuberculosis of the last century, we have crime, violence, isolation, mistrust and mental disorder.

Once our home is unsafe and insecure, it's not long before most other things begin to fall apart. It is family life that suffers most in high-rise flats, and this particularly affects disadvantaged families. It is especially difficult for women and children who spend so much of their time at home. Social isolation is a major problem. For women, the higher up they live in a high-rise block, the more likely they are to show psychiatric symptoms.[27,28] They have feelings of insecurity, and worries about children falling out of the windows or off balconies.[29] Just as we need to feel safe within our bodies, so we need to feel safe within our home,[30] which contains possessions that express our individuality and identity.

Where possible, we try to have a room or at least a part of a room that is our own. In many large institutions, even a small private locker that is personal and owned and safe can, along with the possession of things like a comb and a toothbrush, do much to give us a sense of pride and identity.[31] In human beings, the idea of territory – owned space – has extended into 'owned things', which can be bartered and exchanged – the beginnings of all economics. If these 'owned things' cannot be stored or kept safely, the individual is deprived of something quite fundamental and experiences loss of pride and self-respect.

Just as our home is an extension of our body, so the territory around our house needs to be safe and secure. If it is not, then the house itself will feel unsafe and insecure and those living within it will begin to suffer distress and possibly even illness. Much 'high-rise' architecture, as well as preventing normal social regulation through communal exchange, sharing and self-interest, also prevents the defence of the territory immediately around it. This lack of defensible space has been identified as yet another major cause of personal insecurity and is directly correlated with high crime rates in many cultures, particularly in West Europe and the United States.

Alan F. had just left Acting School after a very succesful three-year course. He was unable to find work but needed to stay in central London to be on hand for acting jobs and auditions as they came up. His early childhood had been rather unsettled but he had managed successfully to put all those feelings behind him. All went well until economic pressures forced him into a 'squat'. There he tried to set up home on his own in a damp flat in the Surrey Docks without electricity and with a number of broken windows. He was excited by the challenge and adventure of all this. He saw himself as an artist living on the left bank of Paris, dispensing with material comfort to pursue his career with dedication.

He was lonely in his new 'home'. There were strange noises at night and fights when the pubs closed. On two occasions strangers tried to break in and then he was served with an eviction order. He began to see and hear things when nobody was there. He became suspicious of people passing in the street because he often felt he was being watched or followed. He became increasingly anxious and was unable to sleep and finally, in a state of despair, presented for psychiatric treatment. With medical help he was able to get a new flat and, two months later, his symptoms had completely disappeared. Five years on he is a successful actor in the London fringe and has no sign or symptom of any mental illness.

There was nothing wrong with Alan in the first place, but a great deal wrong with the space where he tried to live.

Although we may feel our wish for a home is culturally determined, it is probably very much like the territorial behaviour in animals and is to some degree genetically determined. Genes affect the way the mind is formed – and, to a degree, influence how it functions. We have certain built-in responses that may be likened to a computer programme and that we do not need to be taught. These built-in programmes probably operate variably at different stages of our development. Some involve very simple responses like the baby's tendency to suck at the breast, some influence more intricate activities. They are known as epigenic rules. A good example relates to the incest prohibition which is an almost universal feature of human behavour. It seems likely that an epigenic rule exists that inhibits sexual intercourse between individuals raised closely together during the first six years of life. This rule gradually becomes incorporated into culture which then in turn reinforces the epigenic aversion. In a similar way it seems there may be an epigenic rule relating to 'a safe habitat'.

Over thousands of years this basic tendency to acquire or construct a safe habitat or home begins to express itself in culture and may be seen in a variety of forms in different cultures. This built-in tendency makes a major contribution to 'evolutionary fitness' and survival. Without this safe space childcare, food preparation, intimate activity and sleep would all carry considerable risks.

If we think of the risk involved in going to sleep, we can see at once how a secure and defensible home becomes essential to this basic need and vital for our psychological well-being and health. Deprived of sleep we soon become irritable and feel tired. Sustained sleep deprivation has been observed in the laboratory and unfortunately is now a standard technique in brain-washing. The subject becomes increasingly disorientated and finds concentration difficult, and eventually begins to hallucinate and experience terrifying visions. Loss of control often occurs.

The vital importance of sleep has always been recognised and for many cultures sleep has been regarded with awe and mystery. The Greeks linked sleep with death, while among the ancient Egyptians there was a common belief that the soul would leave the body during sleep to return just before waking.

Sleep is usually very difficult without conditions of security, safety and diminished stimulation. Wendy P. was a student nurse in her second year. She was still living in the Nurses' Home when an intruder broke into her room at quarter past two in the morning. She saw the shape of a man and realised he was holding a knife. She told herself over and over that it was a dream, but of course it was not. She spent the next hour in fear of her life and in fear of rape. Fortunately she survived without harm, by talking him down and telling him where all her money was. He took two weeks' savings and jewelry given to her by her grandmother. Long after the shock had subsided, she was quite unable to sleep in that nurses' home and now, six years later, she frequently wakes terrified. The night-time brings on fear and her bedroom is not a safe place any more.

As anybody who has had difficulty sleeping knows, it is almost impossible to will yourself to sleep. Going to sleep in fact involves an absence of will and a surrender of assertion. In such conditions, we experience ourselves drifting off to sleep. Gradually we lose contact with our environment and then with ourselves, and within the disembodied world of sleep we may then experience and remember dreams. These dreams are in fact well correlated with brain wave changes and a form of sleep known as rapid eye movement (REM) sleep. People who are continuously disturbed during their rapid eye movement sleep become extremely restless and begin to suffer from quite marked mental instability. Sleep is not only essential for our bodies but also for our minds. The autonomic nervous system also shows a good deal of activity during sleep and initiates intermittent automatic sexual arousal, clearly visible in the male as periodic erection of the penis.

Having reviewed some of the biological and psychological aspects of our lives, let us look more carefully at the cultural expression of this need for safe space – space that becomes ever more important when the city outside is hostile and unsafe. Our needs for safe, secure territory, privacy and personal space all find expression in a safe home.[29] Law and convention seek to protect this and, throughout the world, the threshold is the dividing line between the public and the private. A knock on the door is a basic courtesy before entering even a close friend's home. Children at play will endlessly build small homes, camps or nests, often in their own house or garden. A.A. Milne wrote a poem about it:

> 'I have a house where I go
> When there's too many people,
> I have a house where I go
> Where no one can be;

I have a house where I go,
Where nobody every says "No"
Where no one says anything – so
There is no one but me.'[23]

The Greeks built homes of mud bricks. Sometimes the walls were so soft that burglars could dig their way in (burglars in Greece were known as 'wall breakers'). For the first six years of life a child stayed at home protected by the mother and enjoying a life that was 'free of sorrow, fear and pain' in the first three years, and full of sports and games in the next three.

In the ancient world mystical and spiritual causes were seen as underlying most phenomena. In order to satisfy their biological and cultural need for a secure home, a safe space, our forebears quite reasonably sought not only to make their homes physically secure but ritually protected in a religious or mystical way. An exaggerated form of the power of the safe space of a home may be seen in the idea of sanctuary. Here offenders against the law were free from arrest, and up to 1697, when sanctuaries were suppressed, several parts of London were treated as sanctuaries. Originally a sanctuary was a patch of open land regarded as holy. Sanctuaries later became associated with man-made structures and were often places of asylum for criminals.

Our attachment to places, although certainly involving safety, does involve many more subtle factors. The association of place with meaning exists not only at a private and personal level but also at a public and cultural level. All of us value and love the familiar places of our early childhood, seaside beaches where we went for summer holidays with our families, old cafes or pubs where we spent good times. Proust celebrates the diverse richness of these associations in recalling his childhood memories of the 'Gurmentes Way' or the Coast at Balbec. On one occasion he trips on a flagstone and this sets off a flood of associations for him. Time and time again he evokes the idea of the ordered, regulated places of childhood and the joy of returning to them.

At a more general level, we revere many old places, particularly those with historic associations. In most big cities of Europe, old houses with mature gardens and worn flagstones fetch much higher prices than the new equivalent and a sense of security associated with family life and continuity is evoked. Just as readily in the garden of a grand house like that of the Vettii at Pompeii as in a small thatched cottage in the Devon countryside.

For a time, some town planning disregarded the old and swept it away, but increasingly planners seek to return to old warehouses or quays or even pavements that are well trodden and beams that are ancient and well used as these have a quality that new stones and wood cannot possibly have. Although there are many components to this feeling, it seems probable that the idea of continuity over time, of others having gone before, and of a place being well used, relates in no small way to a feeling of safety and security. It is the notion that others have been here long before me and will be here long after me. For a moment we lose the isolation of our uniqueness and are absorbed into the continuity of successive generations of humanity.

Towards the end of the twentieth century our need and wish for a secure home is no less intense, but it does seem that its availability is diminishing with serious consequences for us all. Half the women in London are now afraid of rape, even in the daytime. Many are reluctant to travel on public transport. Most old people will not go out alone at night. Many parts of the big cities are almost no-go areas after dark. All too often there is no safe home to retreat to. Corridors and walkways are more dangerous than streets, front doors are kicked in and apparently friendly callers are often menacing thieves.

There is nowhere to run. The cities and their streets have become dangerous, threatening and unsafe. The places that were supposed to be homes in the crowded tower blocks have become as dangerous, threatening and unsafe as the streets, and the families that people try to build around them seem to fall apart. Material and personal safety are eroded, but there is something more subtle and perhaps even more serious, and that is the disappearance of shared values, shared meaning and common purpose. People are becoming isolated and alone. They do not belong to groups or communities or have shared beliefs.

For many of those living in the cities much of the world is experienced second-hand. Many of life's fundamentals have all but vanished from everyday experience. What do you know of heat and cold, trees and fields, birth and death if your only experience of them is on the television or a cinema screen? What do you know of love, care and kindness if nobody has ever loved you or been kind to you or cared for you?

It's not just that we have lost constraints, we have lost touch with what it means to constrain. We have lost track with reality and certainly lost touch with a common reality.

'One sticks one's finger into the soil to tell by the smell in what land one is: I stick my finger into existence – it smells of nothing. Where am I? What does this world mean? Who is it that has lured me into this thing and now leaves me there?'

A new and lost generation emerges with only perplexity to pass on to its progeny. 'Estrangement breeds loneliness and despair, the encounter with nothingness, cynicism, empty gestures of defiance.'. . . Without answers and direction, each feels estranged and alienated from the next. There is no common frame of reference, no common bond or common purpose. The safety of a shared view of the world, of a common theology, of an accepted account of the way things are, no longer exists.

Without common purpose the self, its cultivation, expression and indulgence have replaced communal effort. Consumerism promised us everything. In the city we could buy everything we had ever wanted. Man and woman grabbed at these new models of the world and in them saw the chance for the omnipotence that each of us dreams of as a helpless and vulnerable infant. Here we would triumph over ourselves, the unknown and the constraints of the world. Here at last was the power of the gods. With this went liberation from our frailty, a denial of our true nature and of life as it really is.

In the name of progress, production, self-expression and sexual enlightenment, the whole train of social organisation is losing its way. Newspeak, double-speak, duplicity and media management become the order of the day and nobody knows what they are doing and why they are doing it. Perhaps Moloch is finally amongst us – Moloch whose blood is running money, whose fingers are ten armies, whose breast is a cannibal dynamo, whose ear is a smoking tomb.

Chemical tranquillity, electronic illusion and violence are the enduring symbols of the city and its population's response to this flawed and threatening new world. The brain and body still assert their demands and they have to be overruled. All too often violence becomes not only an appropriate response to lack of safety and estrangement, but a cultural and 'spiritual' symbol that unites and protects a society under siege. Large sections of the community are used to violence and brought up to a culture of violence. As well as being angry, resentful and envious, they are deprived and they feel deprived, and their target all too often is those who they see as having more than them.

Here then, living in fear, is a society and a culture in which there is ample opportunity to learn not only the practical aspects of violence but the social uses and functions of that behaviour. Here is a society in which that conduct becomes adaptive. It works, at least it works better than other styles, and because it works, its use is encouraged. In a world which is seen as predominantly dangerous and threatening and very unsafe, Rocky and Rambo present one way of dealing with the problem. Invincible, all-powerful and with just enough humanity to make them plausible. The ever increasing popularity of violence as entertainment and the collusion of business and government with it suggest that all this is more than just a way of making money. The public want to see it, the writers want to write it, the producers and directors want to create it. Children witness hundreds or even thousands of murders on the television before they are adults (but interestingly, no or few acts of lovemaking, although kissing and embracing are permitted).

What kind of culture colludes so readily with all this? Why are there hundreds of liberal intellectuals who will flock into the court rooms to support all this? The public violence must fulfil some other collective cultural purpose, some horrific exorcism, some smug assertion of our own community, and what it fears above all else but will not admit to. If the man on the screen is being brutalised and tortured it is him and not me. There is also some element of habituation – we are seeing it and getting used to it and not caring about it.

When there's nothing worth doing in the outer material space, then inward retreat to the mind space becomes ever more attractive. But the beep beep flash of computer games contains an interesting give-away. This is no whimsical electronic meditation, no passing amusement, but ritualised combat, confrontation and violence. Here the estranged endlessly act out, with a stylised and ever more abstract foe, the defiant pursuit of safe space, assertion and triumph. In 'space invaders', the most popular of all the arcade games, crudely imaged, but clearly threatening alien monsters multiply and become more threatening and ferocious as the game progresses. The game's sole object is their destruction and presumably the player's survival.

There is layer upon layer of self-deception, layer upon layer of defence. Who we are and what we feel are lost. Feelings don't exist, or if they do, they are a joke, a weakness or symptoms of mental disease. Yet somewhere there are people – people crying out to be heard and understood, people who are not afraid to admit to fear, people who are brave enough and tough enough to acknowledge their own needs and respect the needs of others.

Many drugs of dependence effectively blot out a material world that is meaningless, hopeless and unsafe, and an inner world that is fearful and demoralised. Drugs not only deaden the fear responses of the limbic system – the emotion generator of the brain – but also cloud the consciousness of the cerebral hemispheres, the information processor. William Burroughs puts it like this:

> .. I must report virtual absence of cerebral event. I am aware of your presence, but since it has for me no affective connotation, my affect having been disconnected by junk . . . The Dead and the Junky don't care . . . They are inscrutable.[40]

Of course, there are subcultures and peer group pressures to use drugs, but these exist in part because those drugs fulfil collective needs and purposes of the group that incorporates them into its subculture.

Living in an unsafe village or city in an unsafe world is, of course, not a new experience. It was exactly this that so troubled the Bhuddist monks in medieval Japan, who got fed up with being unarmed 'soft targets' and developed the martial arts which, although an effective form of combat when the rules are enforced, would be no match for the razor-sharp, three-foot-long sword of the Samurai. The martial arts no doubt served to boost morale in troubled times, even if they never fulfilled their promise of unarmed invincibility. The great sage Lao Tzu, who supposedly wrote the Tao, had to grapple with his problem. How could good and ordinary people conduct themselves in a world at war? To be quite submissive might be to invite attack, yet to be aggressive and provocative might be equally hazardous.[41] The hawk and dove problems posed in 'game theory' are not new.

Writing much later, the English philosopher Thomas Hobbes remarked that his mother gave birth to twins – himself and fear. In his political textbook

Leviathan he outlined a political system that would give security to the common man:

> The condition of man . . . is a condition of war of everyone against everyone . . . No arts; no letters; no society; and which is worst of all, continual fear and danger of violent death; and the life of man, solitary, poor, nasty, brutish and short.

For Lao Tzu and the early Chinese, the political acts and personal conduct were not far removed. The microcosm and the macrocosm were closely related. What a man did on a small scale in his personal life was governed by the same ethical considerations that moved his political conduct. Our grasp of the big world outside must, in part, involve transformations of personal experience into political and social reality.

Is it any accident that a society in which domestic safety is a vanishing luxury has managed to build the biggest destructive nuclear arsenal ever assembled? Is not the whole process at best in part offered as another simple and horrific answer to the problem faced by Lao Tzu and Hobbes – wanting to be safe? Could it be something even more subtle – wanting to *feel* safe? Wanting to overcome that fundamental and primitive sense of threat – wanting to do what humanity has always striven to do – to be completely safe.

How else are we to begin to understand the personal condition of other people who conceived of the weapons, voted money for them, and assumed they had a mandate to develop them? Of course, some of them were destructive and cruel and wanted death, but no doubt many were not and wanted to avoid another Pearl Harbour, another Stalingrad, another Belsen, wanted to escape from humanity's eternal vulnerability. Ironically we are now left with MAD, the doctrine of Mutually Assured Destruction. The computers are programmed to ensure that both the assailed and the assailant will not survive. In practical terms this means that if nuclear war breaks out, the world goes. As a strategy designed to ensure safety and survival, it seems to be not quite right.

In his novel *Cat's Cradle*, Kurt Vonegut writes about the observers of a nuclear weapons test. As the bomb goes off one of them says, 'Now man has truly known sin'. 'What's sin?' replied the other. If Hobbes and Lao Tzu came back to visit they would be dismayed and horrified by the way in which technology has magnified and extended beyond imagination our material responses to feelings of insecurity, jealousy, envy, greed and so on. The cost is high and the remedy more dangerous than the malady.

How does all this help us? How does tracing our long journey across time have anything to do with the breakdown of our inner cities? Is an understanding of territory and personal space really going to alter our cities? Well, when we build zoos we try to get the conditions just right. We give the rhino open plains to roam in and the chimpanzee plenty of swinging space and a warm nest to sleep in. Let's therefore try to be clear about what we need. Let's work around an ecology of the whole person. Let's be honest about small gardens for children and pets and plants. Let's not escape or deny our primitive heritage, let's be honest about it. Absence of a safe home is just one of many securities that are being lost, to the detriment of our happiness, stability and adjustment. Unless we start once again to build places for people, respecting the vital importance of a safe external material space, the long term outlook, certainly in the cities, is indeed very gloomy.

The face of many domestic buildings is changing. The arrogant idealistic technological dreams of Le Corbusier are giving way to person-size houses with their own surrounding territory and small common green areas where children can play. In the UK a trust sponsored by the Prince of Wales has thrown its full weight behind community architecture and the redevelopment of run-down inner city areas.

On derelict sites, dedicated community workers build and run adventure parks for the children who live on the twenty-third floor. More and more sports facilities are being built, and in many cities trees are being planted, and disused docks are being reclaimed for public and residential use.

For most of the two million years that we have been on the planet we have lived in small groupings, whose common interest has been survival. Can we once again create small functional groupings in cities and in the country where some useful and practical survival-linked interest unites people? Perhaps a two-tier work system would help, with factory-based high-tech activity and a variety of home-based activities in which a number of families have a share. As the robots take over the technology, and they surely will, really useful and important activities for people become a pressing priority. We can't spend all our lives going swimming in between sessions with an interactive VDU.

Let's be clear that a stable social organisation is a very recent phenomenon and that we still need to work hard to get it right. Let's really try to work out better ways of running small neighbourhoods – where we design buildings and streets for real people. Let's set up power structures and social systems to go with them – not distant centralised local government, but power structures that give at least some important power to the people who live there – power to control what grows in the garden, who lives in the street or the same building or corridor. Power to influence the basic conditions of their lives.

We are not passive creatures and we have the ability, if allowed to use it, to improve our living conditions. Giving more power to the tenants on problem estates does sometimes help. If residents can control who lives with them and who does not, then the enforcement of standards for the common good can dramatically alter levels of crime and violence.[41] We need to be able to exercise control over our own territory and, wherever possible, mechanisms that allow group involvement in this should be encouraged. Without involvement and control, there is alienation, estrangement and despair. We must continue to remember the distinction between space and system. The architect and the planner are beginning to provide the right kinds of space – and the space is vitally important – but that is only the beginning. Within that space will go the living social and family systems that can only be created by people. For the system to exist or function there has to be trust, common purpose and interest. There has to be safe space.

We are beginning to grapple with the spaces, but will the people want to use them? For the cities of the future much of the challenge will involve the dynamics of the domestic social systems – the families, the friends and the extended groupings. For what common purposes will people come together and will they still have enough shared culture to allow them to come together?

7

THE CHILD IN US ALL

A constant source of wonder to early civilisations was the space within the body. This cavity not only created human life but sustained it and fed it and, at the right moment, through one of its mysteries and revered openings, brought it forth into the world.[1] Here was system, space and symbol. Through the mouth passed food and drink, mysterious processes and forces operated within the cavity, and out of the vagina came life. Here was a system that transformed, here was the alchemy of life – not base metal to gold but base food to vital animated flesh. The power of woman's body to transform was readily symbolised by the magic vessel, which became the earth itself. This was the vessel that contained and sustained all living things, the ultimate safe space.[2]

This link between the womb and the world is one that is still useful today, both literally and symbolically. Our scientifically inspired arrogance cannot free us from our dependence on the great vessel of the earth, whilst at the same time the womb continues to remind us of our vulnerability and our absolute dependence on an input of life-sustaining resources. Sadly the eclipse of the feminine has been accompanied by a denial of that dependence and a grandiose assumption that there are infinite resources. Perhaps this is the expression of universal childish longings of both sexes. The world of complete abundance and plenty is never very far away in most religions and metaphysical systems, as in paradise, heaven and even Charlie's Chocolate Factory.[3]

The first interpersonal space – womb and world

If we look carefully at the child's dependence, we will see that before birth its mother, like the world, is fundamentally a life support system, but that after birth, whilst she continues to be a life support system, she also has to become for the child another person – a fellow being.[4]

The provision of safe space with food, warmth, shelter and security has to occur in the context of a human relationship that will become increasingly complex as the child grows and develops. The parallel exchange of the material and personal continues in a variety of forms throughout life, where we are invariably linked with other people for a variety of material ends, involving food, money, security and so on, all accompanied by a number of more or less intimate and complex relationships. We shall see that people around us are a vitally important part of our environment.[4]

The mother, parent or family give to the child mentally, bodily, personally and materially. Within this sustaining system the child is able to grow, trust and flourish. The child does not, and of course cannot, give back much materially, but the child's satisfaction is able to relax and reassure the mother. The sucking and cuddling produce pleasant bodily changes in the mother so that the neediness that the child feels for its mother becomes personally rewarding and satisfying for the mother.

In this close relationship the child loves the mother as intensely as an adult loves its lover. Not only is the contact life-sustaining but also intensely pleasurable. Much of the early psychoanalytic work centred on those early years, but most of the ideas were derived from 'neurotic' adults lying on the couch and looking back to their childhood and remembering, trying to reconstruct the truth of all that, across a time gap of thirty or forty years or more.[5,6]

To remedy these deficiencies, a variety of investigators started to look more carefully at what really happened between mother and child, both in the human setting and in animal society. Whilst some studied farmyard geese, sheep and cows, others watched baby monkeys and others observed, in great detail, the development and progress of human infants in a whole variety of different communities. It became clear that a number of general principles operated, both in humans and in animals:[7,8]

(1) Children like to remain as close to their mothers as possible and when close to them they feel safe and secure.
(2) If anything untoward starts to happen they will try to get closer to their mothers.
(3) As long as they are close to their mothers they will feel comfortable and secure and anything that tries to stop or interfere with that closeness will be seen as a threat and the child will protest violently.[9]

The general synthesis was surprisingly consistent. It pointed towards a well-defined social organisation that sustained and respected infant/mother links. There is a series of biological mechanisms that operated almost from birth to allow mother and child not only to recognise each other but to become closely linked, and a well-defined nutritional and caring capacity on the part of the mother to sustain the child. The sum of all this was a safe enough and sustaining enough environment in which the child or infant could grow and develop and learn.

You do not have to be much of a biologist, ethologist or any kind of specialist to note that baby animals are closely attached to mother animals. Young puppies follow their mothers around and so do kittens. Lambs scamper about the field after their mothers. They seem to cling onto the teat of the mother with a fairly ferocious energy.[10]

For the scientist working in the wild state and observing all this in more detail, a number of fascinating facts are observed, many of which are of course well known. Observations showed that new-born animals have the capacity to latch on very quickly to an object with which they made early contact, new-born geese would follow the farmer around the farmyard if they were exposed to him after birth and not to their true mother. This was described as imprinting and it led to the idea that there were special periods of sensitivity in newly born animals that facilitated their attachment to their mothers.[11]

Much of the most important work on human attachment has been that done on monkeys, for there are very close and intimate relationships between mother monkeys and their babies. Interestingly enough there are also fairly close relationships between other females in the troupe and baby monkeys and males in the troop and baby monkeys.[7]

Some of the most fascinating early work on attachment and the feelings of safety it induces were done in a series of famous experiments using dummy mothers.[12] These experiments were quite intricate but in essence young baby monkeys were separated from their real living mothers and were offered alternatives in the form of a wire dummy mother or a cuddly cloth dummy mother. Even if the wire mother was designed in such a way as to give milk, the infants would take milk from the wire mother but then run off to spend more of their time clinging to the cuddly cloth mother. Often they would spend up to fourteen hours a day clinging to the cuddly cloth mother.[12]

The safety engendered by this passive lifeless cloth mother is striking and dramatic. Babies brought up by the cloth mother when frightened would run to the cloth mother for a moment or so and then might even leave her and set off to explore the source of the disruption. By contrast, babies brought up by the wire mother would not run for safety to the dummy mother and neither would they set off later to explore the source of the danger.[12]

In another equally dramatic experiment the baby monkeys were placed in a room with a variety of toys that they had not seen before. If the cloth mother was present in the room the young monkeys would go out and explore these toys, returning from time to time to the cloth mother. If, however, the cloth mother was not present in the room the young monkeys showed a good deal of fear and would scream and cry. By contrast, if monkeys brought up by the wire mother were placed in a similar room with similar toys they would show no daring exploration of the toys, nor would they derive any comfort at all from the presence of the wire mother. Instead they responded with distress and anxiety just like the cloth mother monkeys did when the cloth mother was removed from the room.[12]

In baby monkeys, then, a cuddly dummy mother that cannot even give milk is able to engender feelings of safety and security in those monkeys. In that context of safety and security those baby monkeys were able to go out and explore the world. It's as if those deprived of this early security are never able to enjoy the security and support provided by others and never really come to trust the world.

In the wild state baby monkeys usually cling to the mother's chest or stomach, at first lying beneath her. At around six months of age they climb up onto the mother's back and travel with her in that way, rather like a rider on a horse. As the baby grows up it begins to spend more and more time away from the mother but almost never out of her sight. Only at the onset of sexual maturity does the close physical attachment between mother and baby begin to wane. Even in adolescence the attachment continues and these teenagers will, after spending some time with contemporaries or others, frequently return home to mother.

These experiments are dramatic, powerful and positive, but the story is very much more complex than this. The basic message seems very clear: for baby monkeys and for baby human beings, mothers provide not only an immediate safe space but an umbrella of safety. Within that umbrella the baby monkey and the baby in fact may begin their first exploration of an unknown and hostile world. Deprived of that umbrella, deprived of the intricate security provided by the mother's presence, those babies will remain fearful and this fear and insecurity, it seems, may stay with them for many years and possibly throughout their lives.

In many societies and cultures physical proximity between mother and child is maintained at all times. The child is strapped onto the mother by a large sheet of cloth or some other mechanism, and goes with her wherever she goes. It is always close to the breast and always close to the warmth and security of her body. At night children are not put into cots or cribs or any sort of separate nursery or sleeping accommodation but simply lie down on the bed or on the floor with the mother and sleep with her. In its early stages of development the child is never far from the physical presence of the mother. For the baby this closeness is affirmed in a very special way, by nothing less than the beating of its mother's heart.

A variety of studies have shown that the vast majority of mothers carry their children with the child's head resting against the left side of the mother's chest.[10] This allows the child's head to be in close contact with the mother's beating heart, which of course lies on the left side of the body. It is suggested that the rhythmical beat of the mother's heart is a reassuring and calming influence on the child, and it may be that the comforting effect of the syncopated rhythm finds its origins in this primal signal of safety.[13]

Of course this very close physical relationship to the mother is only present during the first year or so. Gradually as the child grows and develops, it begins to spend increasingly longer periods away from the mother until about the age of four or five when it is able to start mixing more freely with children of its own age and tolerate long periods of separation. This is, of course, the time when most children start going off to nursery school or play school and although they may protest at first, most of them usually make a reasonable adjustment to this, particularly if they can feel at ease with their new teacher or with one or two special friends at their school. Gradually as the child grows and develops, so its attachment to its mother and family begin to diminish in intensity. Applying ideas of system and space, we can think of an intimate personal relationship system being created between mother and child. Both of them are components of the system, but that system, once operating, provides the child as an individual with a safe space in which it is able to carry out all kinds of new exploratory activities and, as it grows, even to start to participate in new relationship systems with its peers.

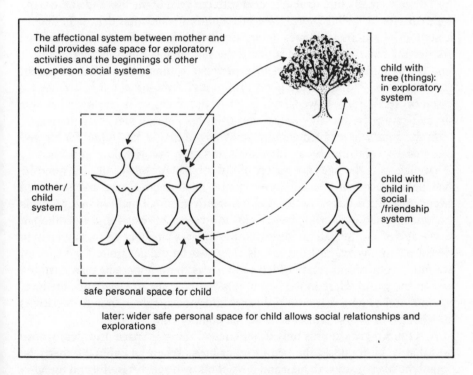

The affectional system between mother and child provides safe space for exploratory activities and the beginnings of other two-person social systems

child with tree (things): in exploratory system

mother/ child system

child with child in social /friendship system

safe personal space for child

later: wider safe personal space for child allows social relationships and explorations

Duncan G. worked in the accounting office of a large and well-known department store in London. He was a rather solitary man in his early thirties, seemed to have few friends and was generally quiet and had some difficulties in mixing with his colleagues and friends at work. He seemed slightly child-like and awkward and was generally the subject of jokes in the office where he worked. He was somewhat disdainful and aloof and had a considerable interest in science fiction. In the evenings he involved himself in a number of voluntary projects, usually with young boys in the East End of

London. Neither his employers nor his fellow charity workers knew that he had already been to court on two charges of molesting young boys under the age of fourteen.

It was only when the scandal of a third offence made newspaper headlines that everyone around him became aware of his previous offences. In the ensuing scandal he obviously lost his voluntary charitable work and also was asked by the management to resign his post in the accounting department. He appeared in court and in spite of psychiatric evidence was sentenced to two years imprisonment. However, a detailed psychiatric report and a social work report were prepared and the central features of these are very relevant to the issue of safe space.

Duncan's mother died in childbirth when he was eighteen months old and his father seemed quite unable to deal with the grief of the loss and at the same time care for his child. Duncan was taken into care and after that spent time in a number of children's homes before finally being settled with foster parents. As a young child therefore he suffered the sudden loss of his mother, the later loss of his father, and went on to experience a number of different parent figures, some of whom were good to him and some of whom had really no concern at all for his welfare. He grew up, then, in a world which was unpredictable, frequently loveless and from his point of view very unsafe.

In the course of detailed enquiries it emerged that he had found for himself one place where there was a modicum of safety, security, love and warmth. That place was the bed of a variety of older boys. At the age of five, when he had been placed in one children's home, he formed a long and sustained friendship with a boy of twelve. He frequently spent all night in bed with this boy and was subject during those nights to a variety of sexual abuses. Although at the age of five he had no idea what the sex was all about and was unable to derive much enjoyment from it, it is clear that he did get from it a degree of warmth, security and safety which to him was more important than anything else in the world. Here in the bed of this boy he came to experience the love, warmth and contact that most ordinary children experience from their parents or siblings, of course without the sexual component.

As Duncan grew up his only experience of the safe space provided by love was that to be found in the bed of other boys. When he entered puberty he found the idea of sex with men and boys of his own age distasteful and found in the presence of women that he often felt nothing whatsoever, while at other times he had a feeling of sickness and despair which he could not account for. For a number of years his life remained loveless and sexless. He lived in a solitary, lonely, fantasy world which was generally rather unsafe, although his involvement in science fiction stories and astronomy helped him to escape from this unpleasant reality. In his late teens and early twenties he became increasingly aware of a powerful attraction towards young children. Often this was not sexual, but it expressed itself in an urge to cuddle and be close.

However, when he was close and was cuddling, his sexual desire began to intrude and he became increasingly tempted to involve himself in sexual activities with young children.

At the age of twenty-one Duncan embarked on his first sexual encounter with a young child who, like himself, was without parents, was lonely, deprived and lacking in love. Clearly there was some kind of self-interest between them, and just as the twelve-year-old boy had exploited Duncan's need for the safe space of love and closeness, so Duncan exploited this child's need. Here in this sexual encounter he found the security that he had first encountered when he was aged five and from then on his desire for children became increasingly strong, ending finally with his two year prison sentence.

Whilst in prison, he became involved in psychotherapy and was able to tease out the basis of why he felt attracted to children. On leaving prison he tried once again to make close relationships with adults, but found this extremely difficult and unsatisfying. He continues for the most part to live a lonely and solitary life in which much of his experience of sexuality and human warmth is based on fantasy. He is continuously afraid that he will offend again as he feels a desperate need for contact with other people. This contact, however, only seems to be possible for him in the setting of an exploiting relationship with somebody much younger than himself – a carbon copy of the only closeness and attachment that he himself knew as a child.

In Duncan's sad story a number of important themes emerge. Without his real mother or any reasonable substitute he eventually went into a state of despair and detachment where people were not to be trusted and where he saw little point in trying to pursue his relationship with them. In this state, at some level he still had a deep craving for the safe space of closeness with another. He grew and developed and eventually went back to the only strong and safe relationship that he could remember; he tried to recreate it for himself and tried within it to experience the safety, love and warmth that he had known so transiently and intermittently as a child.[14]

The safety of this space is not only about getting what you need, but expressing your need, trusting that you will be provided for and being able to communicate your pleasure and satisfaction in a way that is rewarding. (Most children soon get their mothers fairly well trained!) Infancy and childhood involve not only getting what you need, but learning and developing all the time, so that as well as surviving you learn trust, understanding and restraint. The harmony and peace produced by the satisfaction of these diverse desires and needs no doubt offers a prototype of safety that is obviously refined and diversified later in life.

For Duncan, the loss of his mother when he was eighteen months old and the subsequent break-up of his family not only deprived him of safe space at a time when he very much needed it, but also deprived him of the chance to learn from those intense early relationships. Much of this learning has to take place at particular periods in growth and development and, once these are past, it is often very difficult to acquire these capacities at a later date – although it is possible. Duncan needed intimate contact with another and found it, but through an exchange that invariably involved exploitation and was not acceptable to the modern world.[9]

Many children will go to desperate lengths to find that intimacy, that elusive safety and security that caring people can so effectively provide. Those who don't find it anywhere, often become hard, cold, aloof, bitter and resentful. All too often, they are the outsiders – the psychopaths. Their inner rage and anger with the others in society who have what they always wanted continuously boil over into uncontrollable destructive rage. All too often they cannot feel or enjoy the warmth and safety and closeness of human groups, for it is something they have never known and often never can know. Sometimes, of course, the pain and the longing cannot be denied or blocked out, and in some cases alcohol or drugs are then used to blunt the aching loneliness and need. The position is often made all the worse by the mass of people all around who, like the sea water for a shipwreck victim, cannot quench the sufferer's thirst.

It should never be forgotten that the mother, or mother figure, or father, is only the final, common personal focus of a much wider environmental support system involving safety from physical threat, the provision of food, water and shelter, and the involvement of other co-operating adults and children. The true importance of this close mother/child link only became apparent during the Second World War. At this time many children were separated from their mothers and 'evacuated' to the 'safety' of the coast or the country, away from the bombing of the big cities. It was noticed that many responded badly to this. Systematic and detailed observations showed a fairly standard sequence of responses to these separations.[8]

Children over about six months of age when separated from their mothers by, say, a hospital admission or sickness or death, responded in a fairly uniform way. Three stages were identified, protest, despair and detachment.[8]

The initial phase of protest lasts from a few hours to a week or more. During it the young child appears acutely distressed, cries and screams and throws himself about in his cot. Any stranger approaching provokes special interest – for she may be the absent mother returning and this apparent optimism persists for a while before being succeeded by despair. Here the child seems to be giving up, to be mourning the loss. Later still this gives way to an apparent return to more normal behaviour. The child begins to show more interest in his surroundings and to accept attention from strangers – but if his mother now returns he shows no special interest in her. It's as if he has given up on his true love. It's as if he no longer cares. Something within him is broken.[8]

There is something rather chilling about all this. The pain and vulnerability of the child is immediately obvious. The body may grow and develop and the intellect rationalise and make excuses, but at times we can all feel the child

86

within us who loves with such desperation. This love is not so very different from that of the teenager or adult in love.[2] Of course very young children cannot remember all this but older children can, and even some distinguished older children. Proust writing in *Swann's Way*, the first volume of his long novel, *Remembrance of Things Past*, writes of his own intense need for his mother in the following way:

> My agony was soothed; I let myself be borne upon the current of this gentle night on which I had my mother by my side. I knew that such a night could not be repeated; that the strongest desire I had in the world, namely, to keep my mother in my room through the sad hours of darkness, ran too much counter to general requirements and to the wishes of others for such a concession as had been granted me this evening to be anything but a rare and casual exception. Tomorrow night I should again be the victim of anguish and Mamma would not stay by my side.[15]

Ironically, separation often affects those from the privileged end of society, where many young children are sent away to school at the age of six or seven. For some this appears to be a good and positive experience, but for many others it is a shattering and isolating experience in which they are abruptly wrenched from the safety and security of the home and placed in an environment which is full of unknowns and insecurities.

Annie A., a successful lady barrister in her fifties, is unmarried. She recalls being sent away at the age of six from her home in Shropshire to a convent where she was a boarder:

> The whole experience was quite baffling to me. My parents, both of whom had been sent away to school, presented the idea to me as something thrilling and exciting and something which I was bound to enjoy. As the first day of term approached and summer passed I became increasingly apprehensive. I was happy at home, had brother and sisters and friends, and a nurse who had looked after me as a child. I could think of no possible reason to leave my home and the idea of not being able to see my mother in particular filled me with dread. Yet the atmosphere in the house was such that to have said all this would have been an unspeakable heresy. I suppose I was rather glum and quiet when school was discussed, but when anybody saw a certain apprehension on my face, they simply made jolly and supportive remarks which served only to increase my isolation.
>
> When I went off to school it fulfilled all my worst expectations. I lived in a cold unpleasant dormitory with girls who I did not like, nuns appeared in general to be strict and rather punitive, although I did have the odd contact with a kind and warm one. This, in fact, served only to make things worse and to remind me of all the warmth and closeness of my parental home.
>
> I do not blame my parents for sending me off to boarding school. I

suppose they thought it was the best thing to do. However, looking back on it I regard it as a dreadful and terrible experience which gave me very little and took away a great deal. Although I have never been married, I have always urged my own friends not to send their children away and not to collude with social customs just because previous generations have done this.

The convent may have been materially safe for Annie but she experienced it as a lonely, cold and unsafe space in complete contrast to the warmth and safety of her parental home. At the convent she was close to nobody, and neither her fellow pupils nor her teachers were able to provide her with the safe space which she had known in the loving relationships of her parental home.

The effects of parental loss or separation often extend far beyond the pain and sadness of the immediate trauma. It has become increasingly clear that the difficulties that many adults experience may, in part, be traced back to problems at the start of their lives. The growing child develops a picture of the world around it, and with that is able to pick out what is important and what is not. With recognition of mother, or caring figure, and her importance comes not only the actual experience or being with her but also the possibility of being without her.[16]

The psychoanalytic movement regard this anxiety about loss of the mother (or equivalent) as very important to the child, who has to experience it, suffer it and somehow overcome it, partly by getting secure in the real world and partly by using various ideas or mental strategies (defence mechanisms) to make this dreadful and unthinkable threat more bearable. Clearly the mother offers safe space and her absence makes that space very unsafe.[17,18,19] Much reassurance, safety and security is given in the day-to-day physical care of the baby, the touching, the bathing and the feeding. The way that this physical care is given, is delivered, is handled, is of vital importance.[4]

Recall how in a cafe you might sit down and ask for a cup of tea when you feel tired and thirsty. There are a whole variety of ways that the 'tea person' might respond to your request, some of which can be so aggressive and resentful as to wipe out any positive effect from the tea. In a similar way, the child may have what he needs to survive physically, but the messages that have accompanied this care may have been very confusing. If the response to a need is sometimes anger, sometimes irritation, sometimes kindness, then the child will become confused and uncertain. He may not develop the strength of self and personal trust to develop successfully as an independent person who feels generally secure and safe and is able to deal with threats and anxieties in an increasingly effective way.

During the first year of life the passive helpless baby is at the mercy of powerful impulses or desperate fears. If he or she is able to experience a calm, containing, holding mother (or parent figure) coping, containing and providing relief and a feeling of safety, then that child will begin to learn that there is a remedy somewhere. The analysts suggest that this capable calm safe parent figure is 'internalised' and provides a 'model' for the child which later it can repeatedly refer back to and recall when it experiences threats and anxieties.[16]

The loved figure should also be able to tolerate the assaults, the anger and the rage that the child may show when its demands and wishes are not met.[6] To respond to these with anger, sustained rejection or abandonment will set up longstanding insecurity in the child that will be difficult to reverse. The experience of such adequate parenting seems to be a vital part of early development and lays a foundation not only for secure and safe attachment but also for the ability to tolerate limited amounts of threat and anxiety alone. The early experience of safety with the mother or mother figure helps the child to feel safe with others when it is older and also to feel safe in the face of limited amounts of threat.

The Kleinian school have proposed that in the earliest months of life the child has no concept of the mother as a separate unified whole person, but merely as a series of parts with particular qualities (e.g. a satisfying breast full of milk). Later the child comes to realise that its mother is a person that can be either fulfilling or frustrating, succouring or frightening and so on and it has to start relating to this other whole and rather unpredictable person, it has to trust, to forgive and to pay back, reward or sustain. The child will sometimes love and sometimes hate, sometimes sees the mother as good or safe and sometimes as bad and threatening. Gradually it has to bring all the qualities together in the same person. Sometimes this never happens, so that important people are like the little girl in the nursery rhyme who when she was good, she was very very good and when she was bad she was horrid.[20]

The tendency to idealise good and bad, safety and threat is of course a universal human quality perhaps nowhere better expressed than in the Christian idea of God and the Devil, and their respective realms of heaven and hell. Of course many things can go wrong in the mother/child affectional system, but commonly problems occur when, for various reasons, the mother cannot appreciate the signals that the child is giving her – perhaps because she is too hired, harassed or distracted. If things are going wrong, try to look not just at specifics and particulars, but also at you and your child as a system in which each gives to the other. Let the child give you its pleasure and its satisfaction and its love, which it will do if you can give to it. Love is the most important thing. Find the love for them and then express it, and let them feel it and, if possible, let them give it back to you. Start with love but let it be tempered by continuity, closeness, communication and calmness.

Continuity

Children are always fearful that they will lose their supports, their parents, their safety. A certain dependable and predictable quality of life gives a feeling of safety and security.

Closeness

Children like to be needed and to be physically and emotionally close to their parents and those whom they love. Feel their closeness to you, enjoy it yourself and feel them enjoy it and flourish on it. Feel the safety, security and calmness that flows from the combination of emotional and physical closeness. Don't be afraid to hug or cuddle them. Let that take some time so they can enjoy it and be with it and enjoy it.

Communication

Whatever the age of the child, learn to relate to it on a variety of levels – through noise, through touch, through eye contact, through play. Children, like adults, relate in a variety of ways and are stimulated by and enjoy communication. They need to know you care and they will only feel safe and loved if they are aware of your good feelings.

Calmness

It is impossible to be with children without getting cross or flustered or upset at times, but try in general to make the daily contact calm and ordered, rather than hurried and resentful. Much of the early message the child receives come to it through the day-to-day tasks of feeding, cleaning, washing, dressing and so on. If that is done with bad feeling and in excessive haste, the child will sense this and will feel insecure in relation to all those activities and that should make for closeness and safety.

Our own culture, for a variety of reasons, often seems to play down many of the intimate and interpersonal needs that are so important to children. It is not surprising that when we become adults we pay even less attention to these needs even though many of them persist – often heavily disguised. In order to try to escape from some of the restraints of your culture, try this powerful exercise in imagery – particularly when you are feeling lonely or unhappy about some personal relationship. Try to visualise yourself as two people – as the adult that you are but also as a child. You, the adult, are looking after the child that is you. Then ask the child what it wants and why it is so unhappy. Encourage it to talk freely. Some of its answers may surprise you but, if you listen carefully, they may in the long term be very helpful to you. A similar exercise may also be performed with children. The answers are much less surprising but even more important!

8

SAFETY IN LOVE

They walked slowly, hand in hand, along the beach, the warm wind on their tanned naked bodies, the waves gently breaking on the sand. He just stood and looked at her and she at him. At that moment the two of them, who had been longing for each other for so long, finally realised that each really did love the other.

Each was filled with an almost indescribable happiness and exhilaration, the two of them felt now as one and in that simple, and perhaps symbolic linking of hands was the statement of their togetherness, trust, hope and security that each gave to the other. The future stretched ahead, full of dreams and ideals – everything seemed possible. It seemed so good that each felt occasionally that it all just might be a dream – could this perfection be real? Could this really happen? Yet, in spite of the doubts, each knew that it could, that it would.

They sat down on the sand, he lay back and looked at the clear sky, she leaned over and pressed her mouth to his. Slowly, with a long and lingering kiss, their bodies gently met and for the first time. 'I love you,' he said, to which she replied, 'I love you'.

Few of us are strangers to these ideas of true love, and all that they promise. In a changing culture, the ideal of romantic love and possibly subsequent marriage (or a long-lasting relationship) still remains very persuasive for a great many people.[1,2]

At the time of marriage, most people have loosened their links with the parental home and family, and in that new isolation find themselves ready to make new and strong attachments. Their intimate attachments of adult life have so many similarities to the intimate attachments of parent and child that they must be linked in a whole variety of ways. Of course in adulthood we have free will, culture, sexual passion, desire, self-fulfilment and a whole variety of other qualities, but even when all these other factors are considered, the similarities between adult attachment and childhood attachment are striking, yet all too easily forgotten or ignored.[3]

We have looked carefully at all this from the point of view of the child with his or her attachments. Let us now look a little more carefully at marriage and variations of it – with particular emphasis on marriage as a mutually sustaining affectional system that creates a safe environment which, when it is right, can be so supportive and life-giving and which, when it isn't, can be so destructive and harmful.

For many, the ideal of marriage or commitment to a permanent partner is initially a matter of passion that soon comes to embody a variety of other ideas including self-fulfilment, self-expression, a variety of economic goals and frequently a home and children. Closely linked with all these ideas is the idea of the partner as the most loyal and trustworhty of all friends and relationships. Your home, which you share with your partner, gives concrete expression to all this as the absolute embodiment of your territory and your space – in which intimate daily life can proceed and in which children can be born with an excellent chance of survival. A space where you can eat and sleep, live and bath, rest and play and work, all with a sense of freedom and assurance that you do not expect to find elsewhere. A central element of all this is the quality and the strength of the link that we make with our loved partner. (In this chapter the word 'marriage' is used to describe all long-lasting exclusive relationships between adults, whether or not they are formalised by a civil or religious ceremony.)

Being 'in love' is a prerequisite for marriage – yet what is that love? Love is of four kinds, which were identified by the Greeks and the Romans:[4,5]

Sex – which is lust, libido and desire.

Eros – which is the pursuit of the union of lovers – which involves both procreation and an aspiration to some kind of higher and almost mystical union. It is something that also features in many texts on tantric yoga.[6]

Philia – which is friendship – your spouse is usually one of your best friends; and finally

Caritas or Caring – which involves commitment to the welfare of others.

The love of marriage clearly features all four of these loves. At the start, sex and eros often predominate as the passion of romantic love – it is this first stage which so captures and entrances our culture. It is from this stage that the more enduring elements of marriage develop. At the start this two-person system can be an almost obsessional preoccupation for the partners. Their lives centre around each other and they can think of little else.

With the passing of time, the nature of this friendship changes and caring and friendship become increasingly important. At the same time the egocentric focus begins to shift. The lovers begin to start looking outwards to the world.[7,8] Spending all weekend and every weekend in bed seems to be less of a priority. The intense and passionate love has created and consolidated a mutually

92

appreciated safe space in which there is trust and commitment – and perhaps a less compelling need to devote energy to the relationship.

This is a major turning point for marriage. The two-person system is working, the space feels safe. Where are the couple going? What are they going to do with their life together? This stage is known as the working coalition and both reaching it and making use of it can pose problems. Often one partner does not want any lessening of the passionate stage – sometimes because of childhood insecurity and sometimes for other reasons, they do not want to change. They want to be on honeymoon for ever. This can, of course, be achieved by frequent change of partner and does seem to be a popular solution for actors, actresses and millionaires.

All too often the arrival of a child will signal a more abrupt end to the initial honeymoon stage. A two-person system devoted to adulation, exploration and mutual delight is all at once involved in sleepless nights, nappies and earache. If the marriage is not prepared for the transition, it can prove both difficult and at times destructive to the partnership.[9]

We can use the systems model to illustrate how in the ideal marriage the working coalition simply becomes a second system working alongside the first, rather as we may go to work and also be involved in the local church. Some energy remains committed to the two-person romantic system with its love and sexuality, whilst some is committed to the new system – the marital coalition – as the people involved work towards new mutually acceptable goals, such as child rearing.

Sometimes the balancing act is too much and the couple simply abandon the first system, with its love and romance, put that behind them and get down to work. There is little safe space for either partner and the marriage becomes rather like a place of work where the satisfaction at the end of the day is the achievement of a 'productivity target' and a cup of cocoa at bedtime. It was this that so upset Stephen's marriage to be described in the next chapter. Stephen felt that his only role in the marriage was to provide money for the home. He was a worker but not much else.

At times the couple may struggle to sustain the original romantic core, but the pressure and demands of the working coalition are just too much from the start and they begin to drift apart – both suffering from exhaustion and disillusionment. They fail to nourish each other and eventually one or both of them will start to look elsewhere for the safe space their marriage cannot provide. The romantic core will often be abandoned because one partner feels that they don't need it – often in fact denying a deep and inner craving for love and security.

Anne K. came from a rather cold family. Her father ran off with a younger woman when Anne was twelve. As she grew up she was always a shoulder to cry on for all her friends and after an English degree she made a great success of social work. She married an older man who had suffered two minor breakdowns and who over the years came increasingly to depend on her for support. Friends noted in this childless marriage that she seemed almost to be a social worker or mother to him, and he more like a client or a son than a husband. She herself seemed to have nobody to lean on and drove herself increasingly hard, working late at night and doing 'case work' with demanding clients, until she suffered a severe depressive breakdown at the age of thirty-six.

For Anne K. her need to feel safe and cared for was something she had to forgo at an early age. Not only were her family cold, but the father, whom she desperately wanted to care for her and love her and make her feel safe, actually deserted her when she really wanted him. To survive her deprivation and insecurity she fooled herself about how independent she was, about how she did not need looking after (when of course she did and really all of us do at least sometimes). Being looked after was something other people needed. In order to sustain this belief, she went around looking after other people and denying that need in herself. Her own longing and insecurity became greater and greater until finally, exhausted by running away from what she most needed and exhausted by proving to herself that she did not need it, she had a breakdown.

Now in reality the needy child goes on living in all of us and even when we are adult, that fragile part needs to get support and care and love and to feel safe.[2] Part of being an adult is to be able to look after ourselves, to stand up to the big bad world and not to collapse in a heap every time we feel under pressure, but part is to admit that sometimes we can ask for help and to be looked after and not lose face. The child within us has needs but so does the adult and these too must be met.

This balance between dependence and independence is very difficult to get right, and extremes in either direction often place great strain on ourselves and those around us. This is not just idealised romantic speculation. Many studies of men in particular show clearly that close supportive marriages protect against a variety of stress-induced disorders – most especially coronary heart disease. The hormonal responses to threat and lack of safety over a long period of time produce damaging physical changes in the heart. The right kind of marriage can protect against these.

Those men who rate themselves as enjoying intimacy and support have lower levels of cholesterol and more active immune systems[10]. Prolonged marital stress is equally damaging to the health of women and can affect their mental and physical health in a variety of ways. In Chapter 12 we shall look in more detail at how the safe space of a good marriage actually affects the internal physical environment of the body, acting through the autonomic nervous system (described in Chapter 5) to produce positive bodily changes.

With the development of the working coalition and the increasing role of friendship and co-operation, we begin to see our partners as they really are.

The idealisation of the initial stage has to give way to a more real and balanced picture of our partner with all their good and bad points. Untidiness, moodiness, selfishness all start to feature in the life of a once perfect human being. The emergence of the true self may not be welcomed by one partner who feels let down by the failure and faults that they find. 'I thought I married a "real man" and all I got was him!'

Intolerance or rejection of the partner's real qualities may make the marriage a very unsafe place for them to be – the only way to survive is to pretend – but you can only fool some of the people some of the time. This is shown rather well in one of Ernest Hemingway's most powerful short stories, *The Happy Life of Francis Macomber*. On the surface Macomber seems to be doing all right. He is off on safari in Africa with is wife Margot. She is an elegant, beautiful and, one presumes, rather aristocratic woman, who turns out to set very high standards of male behaviour, and seems not to have much respect for the idea of safety in marriage, or the reality of her husband as a person. He fulfils his role, he is an ideal husband – beyond that he doesn't matter.

He and the elegant Margot decide to go hunting where there are some quite big and wild animals, and Macomber finds himself feeling very afraid. The writer makes it clear in the story that this is a very serious loss of face, something Macomber must overcome. Macomber, Margot and the professional hunter, Wilson, decide to up the stakes and go for lion, but when Macomber meets one the feeling of threat to his safety is so great that he starts to shake and cannot fire his rifle.

Margot grabs the rifle and fires in the direction of the lion, but hits Macomber in the back of the head and kills him. It is not clear in the book whether she was trying to save his life or she killed him because he was not man enough. With Hemingway the latter seems to be more likely. Many of his male characters are tied up with aristocractic women who seem to be viewed as some kind of challenge or test for the man in question. The argument perhaps runs like this: she is vicious, tough, beautiful and very high class. The author seems to imply that if you can handle her then you must be a real man.[11]

At times, of course, it is the protagonist who does not wish to be aware of the truth about himself or herself and seeks to get through the marriage in a false position, relating to the other partner rather as if they were a mirror reflecting back to them the picture of themselves that they want to see. Sean was a large, tough-looking man who was the son of a large, tough-looking man. Sean's father was fairly clear that real men did not have feelings and should not have feelings. He pursued detachment and coolness and prided himself on not showing weakness. Believing in these qualities, he was determined to have a tough son. Unfortunately, his commitment to 'manliness' prohibited warm or intimate feelings between him and his son and to make sure that these never intruded to 'soften' the iron man he was moulding, he kept his distance from the growing boy and limited his contact to rather formal exchanges and plenty of gifts, for there was no shortage of money.

As he grew up Sean had no closeness to a real man but became increasingly bound up with his own fantasy of himself, and his father's fantasy of what he should be like. Of course he had a collaborator in all this – his father, who saw in his son's appearance of toughness a mirror for the qualities he so prided in himself. The problem for Sean was that there was not much reality on which to base all this. Somewhere within was a rather lonely little boy who wanted a Daddy to love and who feared he would never be strong enough or tough enough to live up to the impossible ideals of this unapproachable man.

Sean was surprised that he was not very successful with his O level examinations and rather impulsively, but with great faith in his own potential, left school and got a job selling home computers. At first all went well, the market boomed and he had money to spend. To the outside world he was the son of his father. He borrowed money to buy one of the most expensive gold watches and he took to drinking double whiskies and buying rounds. All this greatly impressed Sheila, who worked in the sales records office. Her father was rather like Sean's and she had always wanted to marry a man like Sean – so she did.

All went very well for a while. Sean really became the brash, rather good, aggressive, successful man that he had always believed he would be. In Act Two things changed. The market became saturated with home computers and the public began to lose interest. Much of Sean's earnings had been commission and thus it fell drastically.

Sean was pursued by a terrible empty sinking feeling. He would wake early in the morning and he became increasingly short tempered. At home, however, he showed no sense of self doubt, insecurity or concern, and he never discussed his falling income. He began to stay later and later in the pub and his consumption of doubles became renowned. In the pub he also remained brash, successful, tough and behaved like this, to some degree, at home. He began to drink more and more and was increasingly critical of Sheila if there was any small thing wrong with the home. He seemed angry much of the time (which of course he was) and, when drunk, began to hit his wife, who after eighteen months of marriage realised that Sean was not the man she was looking for and walked out on him.

Sean shows a number of very complex problems, in particular his failure to establish a real and safe relationship with his father, his collusion with his father's face-saving fantasies, his inability to have honest and close relationships with other people, in particular his wife, and his progressive alienation from his 'real self'. For the purposes of this discussion, however, it is the unsupportive and unsafe marriage which is of interest.[12]

Sean and Sheila chose each other because they were both looking for a remedy, looking for a fantasy. An unwritten rule of the marriage was to preserve that at all costs. Sean drank to preserve it, and Sheila did not want to know anything other than the make-believe he brought home to her in the evening, and she did not mind that. What she could not take was the drink and the violence, which of course was the price that Sean had to pay to sustain the make-believe. The marriage offered a very unsafe space, for any deviation from that fantasy was unacceptable to either party.

Of course it is easy to see that, as the real world became hostile, Sean needed safety and support. He needed to share and to assess what was really happening, but this was difficult for him because of his family background – anything but the truth. He would have had a better chance if he could have talked freely to Sheila and tried to weigh up what was going on and what he should do about it. Had he done this, Sheila might have been able to affirm that she would stand by him and still care for him even though he was in difficulties. In reality, of course, she did not much care for him in that situation.

Sean desperately needed help – all kinds of help – to sort out his own response to the crisis, to deal with his own drinking, and of course to help him find a new job. Support would not have solved Sean's problem but it would have helped. Had Sean had a different relationship at work and in his social life, he might have been able to get some support there. He might have discussed the problem with a friend in the pub. All this was impossible because of the fantasy that he was committed to preserve. He responded like the Samurai of Japan – to save face at all costs – but when he did that it did not help him much.

In the midst of all this despair, he should have sought professional help, which for a man in his situation would have been the most practical way of getting support, but this too was unbearable for obvious reasons. Only the bottle was safe, for the bravado and the masculine aura of drink perfectly sustained his own view of himself and, he thought, the world's view. Drink also dulled and numbed his brain. Small amounts neutralised the bodily feelings of fear and with that he lost feelings of wanting to escape and run away. Greater quantities began to muddle the output of the information processor – so he actually stopped thinking upsetting thoughts and forgot about the possibility of his failure. Only the anger remained when he was drinking, anger that he did not understand. The anger was directed against his father for failing in the first place, against himself for being like his father, against the company and the market for collapsing, and finally against Sheila for being 'useless' and not coming in some magical way to rescue him and restore the special powers that he knew he really had.

Before moving on to the emotional and physical conditions that encourage sexual and romantic relationships, let us briefly mention two other ways in which many marriages distort or resist reality.

The first was shown to some degree by Stephen, whose story is told in the next chapter. He became very intimidated by his wife, in part because she had many of the bad features of his mother. We often seem, without realising it, to choose partners who are rather like the opposite sex parent. If our relationship with that parent was good that will present no problem, but if that parent was intimidating or frightening, then quite often we will, all at once, stumble onto the realisation that the person we've married is just like the parent we sought to avoid all along. One woman said, 'I swore I'd never marry a man like my father – I don't want to end up demoralised, over-worked and imprisoned in the way my mother was, then I suddenly realised that he was exactly like my father – in fact in some ways worse'.[13] This sudden realisation goes on to become a blanket judgement which often completely prevents a balanced perception. A successful two-person system is impossible and the marriage runs into difficulties.

Another common distortion, which was seen to some degree in Ann K.'s marriage, involves locating all responsibility for a particular problem or marital task with one partner.[14] Whilst some division of labour is adoptive, polarising can lead to difficulties. One partner will deny all aggression, whilst another will deny all sexual feeling. If there is something we find difficult we can, without realising it, leave it all to the other person. This may work with mending fuses or shopping, but it's not any good if it's affection or discipline or care that's divided up in this way. In Anne's marriage her husband was quite happy to give up all the caring to her.

As love develops it demands a meeting between people, a degree of self-revelation and a capacity to accept both your partner's and your own needs and, to some degree, your partner's and your own weaknesses.[15] If the personal context is right, then the sexuality has a far better chance of success, although clearly much successful sexual exchange can occur, at least for a limited period of time, without ideal personal contact. There are a number of dimensions of safe space created by a personal relationship that seem to encourage and facilitate sexual exchange. We may think of these in terms of both safety with sexuality and safety with our partner.

Although we all have sexual desires and interests in common with other people, there is always an idiosyncratic element about our own sexual pursuits. There are particular things that are right for us and particular things that are wrong for us, and at times these may come into conflict with accepted moral standards. All too often, idiosyncratic sexuality, and for some even sexual pleasure, may to some degree be forbidden. If we are to fulfil ourselves sexually we need to develop a degree of safety with both these elements of our sexuality.

It is surprising how often people are also unsafe, both with their own sexual organs and with the products of their sexual organs. Men often feel self-conscious about the size of their penis and may worry that it is not large enough to satisfy a woman. Some men also feel very uneasy about ejaculating and may not wish to release sperm inside a woman. An interesting variant of this was of course found in much Hindu mythology, and in some other religions, where it was believed that much male strength was lost during an ejaculation.[16] Thus both the ancient Chinese and the Indians practised coitus reservatus, not because they felt unsafe with their sperm but because they felt unsafe about the loss of their strength and energy. Sexuality for the ancient Chinese was regarded as life-giving and an aid to longevity, but only if ejaculation was avoided. Sex manuals from China describe in great detail how this can be achieved. There is also a suggestion that women were eager to gain as much sperm as possible from men in order to use the strength and power derived from this.[17]

It is only recently that women have been encouraged to explore and understand more clearly their own sexual anatomy and physiological function.[18] All through the Middle Ages, women's sexual organs in particular were regarded as shameful and the medieval anatomists named both male and female sexual parts the 'pudenda' or 'shameful parts'. Women's attitudes, of course, are further complicated by society's attitudes towards menstruation and all the mystery that surrounds that. Once again, culture and history have seesawed wildly in their attitudes towards all this and for many thousands of years women's genitals, as well as their sexual function and their capacity to bear children, far from being considered shameful and fearful, were a source of wonder and a manifestation of one of the most potent creative forces in the universe.[19,20,21]

If you are to feel at ease having sexual relations with another person, then it is essential that you feel at ease and safe with your own sexual organs, your own sexual excitement and your own sexual desires. In the last ten years an awareness of this has influenced sexual therapy, counselling and self-help groups. Masturbation and self-exploration, either alone or sometimes even in small groups, has been helpful to people who feel unsafe with these aspects of their own function. Masturbation, far from driving you mad, can help to keep you sane![18]

The fight and flight response also has implications for sexuality, for most men or women will not respond well in a sexual relationship if they experience an excessive degree of fear, anger or threat. The brain's emotion generator can inhibit our sexual responses if there is any feeling of excessive threat or insecurity. The relationship can produce these feelings in a variety of ways. Although the body of the person you love may appear beautiful and desirable, all too often, for both sexes, there is a perhaps unrecognised element of threat in the genitals of their partner. Although some men like to see themselves as penetrating and taking up some active and aggressive role in the sexual act, there is at the same time an element of surrender and risk in male sexuality.

A man's most vulnerable and unpredictable part sticking out into space is engulfed and enveloped by a woman. A man has to trust his penis to his partner's vagina. For many men there is an element of risk and threat here that they often choose not to recognise. Time and time again men, often deeply in love and full of desire for their partner, find that they reach their orgasm prematurely or even lose their erection during the act of love-making. Time and time again, careful review of what is happening in the relationship suggests that there is a hidden element of threat in relation to the vagina, a feeling that perhaps goes back to childhood. Guilt or an element of doubt about performance may also feature, so that the man feels in some way that he is not going to live up to his partner's expectations. Male anxiety in this area is not helped by endless public discussion about depersonalised sex, about sex as a commodity or a game in which one man has to compete with another or to live up to the performance of another man. Sex often becomes a threat when the act of love is divorced from its personal context.

Once this kind of concern and lack of safety has been identified, it can often be helped either by some sort of restrained sexual contact between the partners, where intercourse is avoided for some time, or by some fairly frank and honest discussion about the true worries and concerns.

Women mirror the sexual concerns of men in that they often have anxieties about the entry of an uncontrollable and foreign body into their own bodies. The symbolism of penetration is all too obvious and there may be hidden feelings of fear about damage or injury that can result from sexual intercourse. In women, of course, these fears and anxieties will either cause the muscles at the entrance of the vagina to tighten so that penetration is difficult or painful, or they will inhibit sexual excitement so that there is a lack of secretion or lack of sexual response. When these feelings are present, it is very helpful to try to talk freely and honestly with your partner about them and to let him or her know exactly what you are feeling.

It can also be helpful to be inventive and ingenious in such situations and to pursue sexual exchange and stimulation without full intercourse, so that both partners can still enjoy a closeness, intimacy and excitement, without the risk and threat that goes with penetration. Gradually, confidence may return and some degree of penetration can be achieved. Of course, at times some sort of professional help and counselling may be required as well. The emotional and physical exchanges in love and sexuality can be seen as the expression of a two-person system, but for that system to operate there must first be a safe space. The material requirements are obvious – we would not choose to make love on a motorway or crowded train, but the emotional component can easily be forgotten. We need to feel safe not only with our bodies and sexual parts but with out partner, and the feelings that they have for us. It cannot be emphasised strongly enough that most sexuality has to be seen in the context of a relationship between two people in a particular setting.

Rather as with behaviourism, the development of the Masters and Johnson approach to sexuality had the effect of taking it out of context and looking at it as some kind of physical attribute that could be trained and worked on.[22] There is a small element of truth in this, but in general sexual relationships are expressions of feelings that people have for each other and involve something that people wish to share with each other. At times sex may be sex for pleasure or a way of getting to know somebody, and although some may find moral objections to this, if both partners are consenting adults and honestly know what they are doing, then they perhaps have a right to collaborate in this way. If, however, sex is concerned with a loving and deep relationship, then it will invariably express much of that relationship.

In the context of a deep and close relationship, sexual love is pleasure and delight, but it also carries meaning. A kiss or a caress is pleasure, but it is also you saying something to your partner. It says things like 'you matter to me', 'you are beautiful and special to me', 'I care about you', 'I want to be as close as I can to you'. The meaning that we intend with our caress and our kiss may not be the meaning that the receiver of that kiss or caress ascribes to it.

Peter W. and Sue W. had been married for three years. Their first child was a year old and Sue was still very tired. She was breast feeding and the baby would still only take small feeds. Peter used to want to make love in the evenings when she felt very tired. She quite often refused his advances. When he cuddled up to her at night and kissed her, he was trying to say, 'Let's get back together now that the baby is growing up – let's try and find the special feeling that was between us when we first married'. He was very excited and felt a great deal of desire for her.

For Sue, who was tired and worried about the baby's feeding, this passion seemed something rather out of place. 'How can he really be considering me and our child? Can't he see that I'm preoccupied and worried and very tired?' She began to feel rejected by the very advances that were intended to produce the opposite effect. He began to feel rejected and unwanted and, although he loved the child, he felt it was coming between them and began to wonder if he had any place in their life, except as the breadwinner and as a contributor to the care of the child.

Similarly, if our hearts or our wills are not involved in our sexuality, then once again the response and involvement will be seriously impaired. If a sexual relationship with your partner has been satisfying and fulfilling and then it begins to change, it is important not to look upon this as some kind of defect in machinery, but first of all to look at it as some expression of a relationship between the two of you and the space created by that. It is important to try to talk about the problem and also to talk about the feelings that go with it. Often some element of threat or lack of safety will be at the root of the problem – the space between you is not safe.

Most of us need close relationships with other people, and for much of our adult lives sexuality is the material medium which helps us to make this link with another human being. It is rather like cement in a good wall, which will stand without cement but it's often a lot stronger with it. It's something like that but, of course, it is so much more and only the poets and the romantic writers can really begin to do justice to it, and even they often don't get very close.[19]

Although the emphasis of this chapter has been on the intimate two-person relationship as it occurs in marriage or an equivalent union, we cannot cover the subject of safety in relationships and sexuality without returning to bodily and material spaces, for it is here that a major new factor has intruded which threatens to make much romantic and sexual activity very unsafe indeed.

Nearly five hundred years ago, in 1493, when Charles VIII of France was laying siege to Naples, syphilis, or the great pox as it was then known, appeared in Europe. It spread dramatically throughout Europe, causing as much damage, havoc and disease as the Black Death. It was probably spread by various armies, mercenaries and those who followed them about throughout Europe. There are sinister echoes of this today in the rapid spread of HIV, the virus that causes Acquired Immune Deficiency Syndrome, or AIDS, which is now endemic in a number of African countries and threatens to become so in the West.[23]

In the early stages of the outbreak in the West the people particularly liable to infection were those in high-risk groups, which include promiscuous homosexuals and intravenous drug users. It is now becoming clear that, as in the African countries, the disease is beginning to affect heterosexuals who can spread it to each other.[23,24] The more sexual partners a heterosexual or homosexual has, the greater the risk of contracting AIDS. The pursuit of safe sexual relations is now a matter of great public concern and importance.[25,26]

New codes of sexual conduct and manners are going to have to be scrupulously observed if we are not to have a modern plague. Unprotected intercourse becomes a high-risk activity and even a deep kiss could possibly transmit the disease, for the virus has been found in saliva and could possibly gain access to the blood through an abrasion on the lips or in the mouth. Transmission by this route is not yet proven.

Absolute fidelity is of course one answer but, particularly amongst the young, sexual experimentation will be difficult to avoid. We are strongly drawn to physical intimacy with other people who attract us and often this involves so much more than just a cheap thrill or a quick orgasm. New approaches to intimate physical contact will have to be found and made acceptable to both partners, who will have to avoid any possibility of exchanging body fluids in order to be absolutely safe.[28,29]

The initial high incidence of AIDS in the homosexual population was at first thought to be related to anal intercourse, the virus present in sperm gaining access to the blood of the recipient through the damaged lining of the rectum. Receptive anal intercourse was and still is a major risk factor.[30,31] It now also appears that having several sexual partners is also a major risk factor in homosexuals or heterosexuals. Although women can and do infect men, it seems that the virus passes more readily from men to women, perhaps entering through minute tears in the vaginal skin or perhaps even through intact vaginal skin. Certainly heterosexual men and women are more liable to infection if they have pre-existing genital infection. There is some correlation with herpes in the West or gonorrhoea or chancroid in Africa.[25,26] Yet to be explained is the ability of some 50% of partners of AIDS carriers to escape the virus, even after numerous sexual encounters. A strong and healthy immune system may play a part in this resistance.

For all these anomalies, one thing is clear – AIDS has made most kinds of sexual contact outside a faithful constant partner potentially very unsafe. Once contracted the disorder seems to be without cure, so as with the great epidemics of the past, the best remedy is to avoid contracting the disease. By 1990 the US plans to spend two billion dollars a year combating the disease, whilst many other countries are promoting safe sexual practices through huge advertising campaigns.[24]

Exactly how sexual manners and morals will now develop remains to be seen, but although AIDS is new, the risks it poses are not unlike the risks syphilis posed two or three hundred years ago. At this time, causal agents were of course not isolated and the 'gleets', 'clap' or 'lues venerea' included gonorrhoea and syphilis, which were frequently lumped together as different stages of the same disease.[30] Just as the law and public health measures had been successfully used to combat plague in Italy, so attempts were made to fight 'clap' in England by closing 'sweating shops' and 'public baths'.[31] Many sexually active men such as James Boswell wore sheaths made of pig's bladder, but in spite of these precautions he contracted gonorrhoea, which troubled him for much of his life – he suffered nineteen attacks. Sexual intimacy with a loved or liked partner has always been a vital part of human life, and its moderation by medicine and morality is integral to civilised society.

AIDS poses new and special problems that we must face up to and overcome.[25] As a first step, honest and outspoken information must be given to all. This perhaps should remind us that, although sexual intercourse is a major part of sexual exchange, it is not the whole of it. There is much that two people can communicate and exchange without any kind of penetration. Perhaps the threat of AIDS will bring with it a variety of restrained sexual exchanges which, rather like courtly love and petting, will help us to have at least some safe intimacy with those who attract us and for whom we care.

In good marriages, and in many less good marriages, as well as a variety of other partnerships, there is a very special kind of safe space. It is a space in which there is recognition and acceptance, trust, care and support, a space which, as the years go by, for many people becomes more safe, more secure and more special. Yet marriage inevitably involves personal sacrifice, compromise and restriction of sexual freedom.[15]

In an age which intensely values freedom and self-expression, the sacrifice of these two commodities in pursuit of loyalty and attachment is often too much and many good marriages and close attachments are sacrificed in pursuit of something intense, elusive, unknown and dangerous. All too often the sacrifice of a marriage is closely bound up with the pursuit of passion and of the feelings of love that initially gave birth to the marriage itself.

Nowhere is the absence of reason more clearly seen than in romantic and sexual love, and in no form of attachment are the costs and benefits in such close competition. Often falling in love is anything but safe. A predictable world can be transformed into one dominated by a single, obsessive passion in pursuit of which man and woman will do all kinds of irrational things. The passion, power and pain of falling in love make it anything but safe, but out of the initial frenzy there may grow something solid, lasting and safe which becomes every bit as powerful and every bit as sustaining as the early close and secure contact between parent and child. It is damage to these things which contributes so much to the catastrophe of loss and separation from the loved one. It is not just the loss of the loved one, it is also the loss of what was between you. All at once, the safe space that you and your loved one have created is gone and there may be nothing to take its place. No one else to confide in, no one else with whom to share. That elusive whole of two people who love each other is so much greater than the sum of the parts. Losing a lover, partner or a relationship is one of the most stressful and negative life experiences and is one of the events that quite often precedes attempted or even successful suicide.[32] Although we have reviewed these losses in the context of bereavement, they require a more detailed general examination, for the safe space provided by the love of another seems especially important for us.

The old and young seem particularly vulnerable to such losses, perhaps because they are often rather socially isolated. As the bonds with the parental family weaken, so the young find themselves increasingly isolated in the world. The security and safety that we once enjoyed and welcomed in the parental home may begin to feel rather stultifying and claustrophobic. We feel a great wish to get out into the world and to explore, yet all too often there is a rather painful loneliness and isolation at this time. In this setting, the warmth and intimacy of falling in love are particularly powerful. In a world where the old order is passing, love brings with it the promise of a new order. There is a hint of the new and elusive identity, of waiting but distant adulthood.

Ray came from a wealthy family in which he was the youngest child and only son, with four elder sisters and a rather doting mother. He was sent to a local private school and was successful there, but at sixteen, after O level exams, he insisted on leaving and going to the local sixth form college. He became increasingly distant and rebellious at home. His family had no idea what was wrong with him. A year later he formed a passionate relationship with a girl of sixteen, who came from a rather deprived background. He wanted to leave his 'overpowering' home and she wanted a home – any kind of home.

They moved into a very cheap flat that was due for demolition and while the intensity of their sexual passion grew stronger, everything else about the relationship grew weaker and more chaotic, with constant arguments about domestic arrangements and many petty jealousies. Eventually, after a serious row, Ray's girlfriend went back to her former boyfriend, leaving Ray a note which he found lying on the bed when he got back from college. He was shattered, his life had fallen apart, he had nowhere to turn and no one to turn to. To return to his family would have been to deny everything he had fought for over the previous eighteen months.

There was no safe space within or without. His girlfriend, who embodied all his safe space and his hopes for the future, had gone. He scribbled her a note and swallowed the sleeping tablets she had left in the bathroom cupboard. He had wanted to die, but fortunately succeeded only in sending himself to sleep for twenty-four hours. He's now back with his girlfriend – older, wiser and a little safer – but they are still fighting and each is still threatening to leave the other.

The intensity of these links seems to invoke or relive the intensity of the mother/child link in childhood. Perhaps as in that link, not only are the feelings very powerful but the love is experienced as offering some kind of protection, a feeling of security, a safe space. Some studies suggest that this may be perfectly true. Loving and supportive wives really halved the number of angina causes in one group of men – certainly men may protect their wives from depression and women may protect their husbands from heart disease.[33,34]

Our culture has long recognised these polarities of passion. This love offers safety and fulfilment, but there is the ever present threat of desertion and disaster.

The pain of loss can hurt like nothing else and is a feature of many people's experience. While the 'overdose' and the 'depressive illness' have all helped to 'medicalise' what may be a very noble expression of human feeling, it is really the poets and the writers who take us closer to the pain and the lack of safety in a world without the person we love.[35] Elizabeth Smart's[19] heroine loses the man she loves: 'He is not here he is all gone, there is only the bloated glow. Nothing but the bracelet he put around my wrist reminds me I was once aliive, my dead eye and my blank days only prove I am dead, why not, not his existence.' Later on she writes: 'I am lonely, I cannot be a female saint, I want the one I want, he is the one I picked out from the world, I picked him out in cold deliberation, but the passion was not cold. He kindled me, it kindled the world, love love give my heart ease, put your arms around me give my heart ease.' The intensity of the passion and the suffering when the loved one is lost are all too clear to see without any elaborate explanation.

Ernest Hemingway is commonly associated with very perceptive writing about men at war and men in violent encounters. Hemingway, however, did involve himself in love stories, probably the most famous of which is in *For Whom the Bell Tolls*, although this story is very much bound up with Hemingway's special version of the heroic male. He comes much closer to exploring the pain of love in a short excerpt that appeared in a collection called *The First Forty-Nine Stories*.[36]

> . . . and when he thought he saw her outside the Regence one time it made him go all faint and sick inside, and that he would follow a woman who looked like her in some way along the boulevard, afraid to see that it was not she, afraid to lose the feeling it gave him. How everyone he had slept with had only made him miss her more. How what she had done could never matter since he knew he could not cure himself of loving her.

The pain of separation is all too obvious in these quotations. Perhaps if little children could write with such eloquence and brilliance this is what they would write when they described the separation from their mothers when they were very young.

Infidelity or extra-marital love is often cited as causing the breakdown of marriage. Frequently, however, a variety of other factors are major contributors. A common element in these is their tendency to make the union unsafe, unfriendly and unrewarding. In 1985 in the United Kingdom, unreasonable behaviour was the most common reason for divorce, with decrees granted on this basis against 57,000 husbands and 7,000 wives. In that year there was a total of 160,300 divorces – a rise of 11 per cent.[37]

We may go into marriages for all kinds of reasons, but we tend to leave marriages that make us feel insecure, unloved, unrecognised, inadequate or threatened. We can tolerate these things for limited periods in the outside world, but seem to find them impossible to bear in marriage. Of course, some conflict and confrontation occurs in most marriages, and if this is not accompanied by excessive threat or violence it can be tolerated and accepted. What we cannot accept is a major erosion of our safety within the marital coalition. Here, well recognised and destructive activities such as violence, drinking and gambling are major contributors. Along with neglect and extra-marital relationships, these behaviours, combined or singly, produce a climate of insecurity and distrust and threat, which leads us to feel that we would be better off without our partner. Sometimes this hope is fulfilled, but all too often divorce can be a difficult and very painful experience which demands a great deal of adjustment. Taken overall, the life of the divorced, when compared to that of the married, perhaps emphasises once again the very literal bonds of safety that are conferred by marriage.

Those who are divorced are more likely to suffer from alcoholism, mental illness or physical illness, and they are likely to die earlier from a variety of causes.[38] The figures must be carefully interpreted, for some of what seem to be consequences may in fact have been causes. Alcoholism offers a good example of this for, as suggested earlier, it is a major factor in reducing safety and security within the marital coalition, which in turn may lead on to separation and divorce. The case of Sean mentioned earlier in the chapter ended in separation and later divorce. The immediate contributing factors to that separation were alcoholism and violence, but it is clear from the example that not only did alcoholism precipitate the final breakdown of the marriage, but the conditions of the marriage favoured the development of alcoholism.

Coping with the loss of the safety of the marital coalition is helped by the presence of a supportive network. A new and satisfying heterosexual relationship also helps greatly. Of course, it is not just the partners who feel the effects of marital breakdown. For children attachment to one parent at least is often disrupted. Guilt, doubt and anger may linger long after and this may interfere, at least for a while, with feelings of stability, security and continuity.

Many marriages are not ideal, but they are often the best possible marriage that we are able to make. Such relationships can provide us with a vitally sustaining safe space that may be hard to find elsewhere. Recognising this and the importance of marriage to all involved might encourage us to choose a little more carefully, and try, whenever possible, to repair damage – and in an age where one third of marriages end in divorce, that is surely no bad thing.

9

FINDING SAFETY AND CLOSENESS

If there is food, there will be few who are unable to eat it. If there is water, there will be few who are unable to drink it, but if there is love and closeness and intimacy there will be a great many who will be unable to experience it. The extent to which we are able to become involved in intimate contact with other people will, to a considerable degree, be determined by the way we are loved and cared for during our own growth and development, and by the values of the society in which we live. We have the potential for close attachment to others, but we can live without that most special of safe spaces. What quality of life we have without it is, of course, a different matter.

The same technology that gives us arcade games and fourth generation user-friendly computer language can simulate a whole variety of human exchanges – ever polite, friendly and tolerant, with about as much feeling and sincerity as the recorded voice that tells us the lift doors are closing. Modification of that technology can give us pornographic videos and rechargeable, multiheaded vibrators, programmed to judder at the optimum frequence for orgasm. Sexuality, neatly disconnected from its human and intimate context, becomes just another appetite to explore, just another kick to 'get off on'.

Where once people 'made love' some now 'have sex', or even 'sex' (not as a noun but as a verb – teenagers say now, 'Shall we sex?' or 'I like sexing with him!'). Implicit in this is the idea that the other person is an accessory in pursuit of 'sex' rather than 'sex' being an accessory in the pursuit or expression of love or the other person.

Perhaps one day there will be no Winston Smiths risking all to experience love in the back room of an old shop. In *Blade Runner* even the replicants (genetically engineered copies of human beings) defied their programming and felt intimacy and loyalty towards each other, even though they had been designed not to have these 'unnecessary' feelings.

The majority of adults still do link up with one other person in pursuit of close intimate relationships and some may later go on to create some kind of 'family unit' and have children, although there is an increasing trend for parents to avoid the traditional marriage ceremony, with one in seven of all births in the UK now occurring outside marriage – more than double the rate ten years ago. Within these close linkages there is, as there has always been, the problem of how to be safe and secure with the other person in some kind of long-term, rewarding relationship. 'All you need is love', said the song, but just needing it is not enough.

For an even larger number of people the wish to love is there but the capacity to love is not.[1] They may want love and closeness and intimacy, but for a whole variety of reasons it eludes them. Frequently we can help each other. Marriage, or its equivalent, allows us a re-run of our parental family, but in a different setting and with new ideas and approaches. Often we can, with concern and compassion and patience, heal each other, reach each other and supply that which is lacking. At other times something else is needed.

Never before have there been more therapies or therapists committed to enhancing some aspect of interpersonal relationships. Choosing from amongst them presents quite a challenge, though many of them have a number of common features in that they involve the experience of an intimate relationship with a powerful 'healing' figure in a controlled and safe setting. It is not possible to examine all of them in detail, so in the single case that follows we shall look at a fairly typical therapeutic experience, designed to encourage the client to understand better his own marital problems and to enjoy and experience more fully the safe space of intimate personal relationships which have eluded him for so long.

Steven H. had always been rather an outsider. He had never been very popular at school, having suffered with allergic asthma as a child and avoided rough games with his classmates. He had always liked women and got on well with them, but when, in his twenties, he began to have serious relationships he found that the 'ideal partner' always seemed to elude him. He tended to choose very attractive and intelligent women whom he idealised. All too often, as he got closer to them, he found that they let him down. He would become increasingly critical of them and eventually the women, who often were very fond of him, found his constant criticism and nagging very unsettling and demoralising and eventually they would up and go, being unable to take it.

As he grew older he became quite lonely and determined to marry, even if he had to 'put up with second best', as he put it to himself. He rather grudgingly entered marriage with Carole, a much younger woman, who worked as a trainee estate agent. He fortified himself with the idea that 'she would change'. He saw himself somehow 'moulding' her into his ideal woman, rather like the unfortunate Eliza Doolittle in *Pygmalion*.

Carole, who was quite an enlightened woman, did truly love him but sought to be her own ideal woman rather than his ideal. As their two daughters grew up she retreated from Steven's criticisms by developing an even closer relationship with her daughters. The three of them felt safe together and had a strong bond of love together. Steven took all this very badly and began to feel increasingly uncomfortable with his wife or family – rather as he had felt with his contemporaries at school. Once again, he was becoming the outsider and responded by hostility and withdrawal.

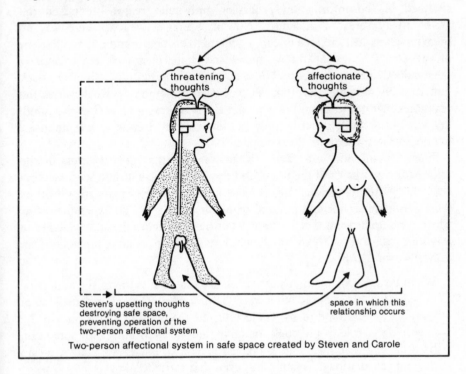

Steven's upsetting thoughts destroying safe space, preventing operation of the two-person affectional system

space in which this relationship occurs

Two-person affectional system in safe space created by Steven and Carole

Steven related his story in this way:

When I get home in the evening I feel as if I'm just about tolerated by my wife and daughters. I earn all the money that pays for the home and the supper and the television that they all watch but I feel I have no place with them. I feel that they put up with me and say a grudging 'thank you', but that they are all happier without me.

At work I'm in charge of a small sales division. The men there seem to respect me, but as the evening approaches I feel tense. The only way I can handle being at home is to drink, or shut myself away with the television or my computer. All this makes me cross and irritable and then I shout at them, which seems to make it all worse. I feel as if they are driving me to it. I've got nowhere to go. I want to tell them all to get lost but that is just what they want.

Here, as so often happens, fear has intruded right into the centre of this man's life, and his home and family which should be the 'safest' place in his world become more threatening than his work. Something about the intimate interpersonal space actually makes him feel afraid in the way that a snake or a wild bull might.

Recall in the chapter on the brain how the sound of breaking glass was analysed in the information processor and quite reasonably raised the possibility of threat and danger. Now in Steven H.'s case there was no breaking glass, just the idea of coming home to his family and it is this that set off all the feelings of threat and fear. Quite clearly there is nothing outstandingly dangerous here. His wife is not planning to beat him or attack him, and his daughters are not yet that good at karate. So what causes the emotion generator to fire off danger signals? It is something in Steven's mind, but something hidden that he does not know about. Let us look again at his brain and the three units that comprise it.

The idea of wife and family is analysed at the highest level, in the information processor of the brain, and this is defined as unsafe, as something threatening and dangerous. In response to this danger, signals are set off by the emotion generator and internal regulator and Steven H. experiences fear which is so unpleasant that he resorts to whisky to neutralise it, or decides to avoid his wife and family by watching television or not coming home at all. In Steven's own words:

> When these problems first started, we used to discuss them. We both tried to be reasonable about it, but it would always eventually end in some kind of slanging match. One of us would lose our temper and storm out. In the beginning Carole would cook something out of the ordinary for supper on Saturday night and we'd go to bed early, hoping, I suppose, that we'd find our old sensual magic again – but even that started failing.

Steven was fairly open, but he found it difficult to talk in any detail about his sexual problems. As his confidence increased, however, he was able to explain how he would become sexually excited in the normal way, but often quite soon after he started making love to Carole, he would lose his erection: 'I don't understand it, I really want all that to work, but as I enter her the whole feeling seems to change. She, of course, thought it was her and asked me why I didn't find her attractive – which of course only made it worse.'

How can we get to grips with the hidden part of Steven's mind that sets off the danger signals and makes what should be the safest of spaces into a threatening, hostile and very unsafe space?

In the diagram is the image of his wife. These incoming stimuli pass into the highest level of the brain for processing. Now here in the processor a strange thing happens. It provokes two sets of thoughts, the first set are conscious and occur to Steven as 'I feel at ease with Carole, there is nothing about her that upsets me', but at the same time in the left-hand section of the 'thinks' bubble there is a second set of thoughts that affect Steven H. but which he does not know about.[3] These may be labelled as unconscious ideas and centre around old memories of his mother when he was very young and when he saw her not as a safe nurturing figure but as a threatening and devouring figure who dominated his father and responded to his childish needs by telling him to 'grow up and be a big boy', so that when he felt most unsafe and most in need he was reprimanded and chastised – these say 'My wife is dangerous'.[4]

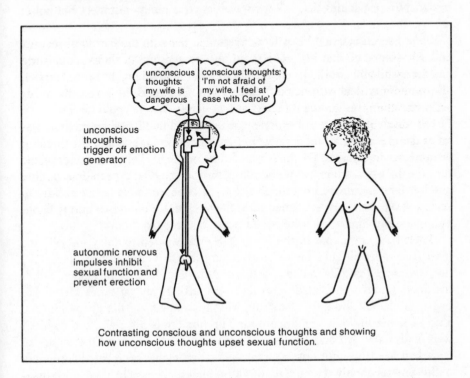

Contrasting conscious and unconscious thoughts and showing how unconscious thoughts upset sexual function.

In order to simplify the role of the brain in safe space the flow of information in the diagram is all one way, from the outside world to the brain and onwards to the various parts of the body. In fact the information processor and emotion generator make very substantial contributions to perception, so that what we perceive owes a great deal to information both intellectual and emotional. Thus the emotion generator (limbic system) gives emotional colouring to many perceptions which in turn may alter our response to those perceptions.

Steven's final view of the world is therefore made up of three components:

(1) what is really going on in the outside world;
(2) stored intellectual memories and associations;
(3) stored emotional memories and associations.

If the stored emotional memories and associations involve a lot of threat and danger, then an apparently safe object or person may in fact be perceived as very unsafe and threatening.

This emphasises clearly, once again, the interreactive nature of perception. Carole, his wife, appears threatening partly because she has become hostile towards him but also because of the way that he sees her. Each of us is particularly sensitive to certain kinds of stress or threat. Similarly, each of us has adaptive capacities that will work well in certain circumstances but not in others.

When Steven married his wife he presented her with the façade of security and self-assurance that his mother had encouraged him to show to the world and for a while this worked well. He became a kind of second father to his wife, always there to deal with her difficulties. Over the years, however, the needy self within him was getting hungrier and hungrier. Where could he turn when he felt unsafe or threatened or lonely, where could he turn when the heat was on at the office and all the men were fighting for promotion and the threat of redundancy hung about for those who did not make it? Things took a dramatic turn for the worse when his mother died, for she had high expectations of him, and her faith in him as a big tough fellow, as opposed to his father whom she saw as weak, somehow sustained him. Steven also looked down on his father and reassured himself that he would never become like him.

When he came home in the evening Steven wanted to show his wife his insecure and fragile side, but he could not for fear that he would be attacked by her, humiliated and degraded. All this and the conflict over it, hidden within his unconscious mind, made him feel very anxious and at times afraid. He began to blame Carole for not doing what he wanted, for not giving him the kind of home life that was organised. The home was not right, the children were bad mannered and finally he began to blame Carole for the failure of what had been up until now a happy and satisfying sexual relationship.

Steven was quietly starving, he was absolutely alone and he was very cross – cross because he was not getting what he wanted or what he needed from his interpersonal world, and cross because in some vague way he knew that the deadening and stultifying coldness of his own childhood had come back to haunt him in his own marriage. He blamed others for all his failures and in particular his wife, and his anger towards her of course still further alienated her and created even more difficulties in his marriage. We may summarise all this as follows:

(1) Put very simply, his problem is that he feels unsafe in an intimate interpersonal space which should be very safe.
(2) The problem at least in part is related to attachment; he does not trust, and he cannot trust, or feel safe with another in an intimate relationship.
(3) The problem goes back a long way to when he was very young.
(4) He cannot deal with the problem because he does not really know what it

is, because much of it resides in a part of his mind that is not accessible to him.

It is quite clear that in Steven's case a great deal of his insecurity and lack of safety is related to these inappropriate perceptions that derive from his past and are hidden from him. In trying to sort out his problem, he will need to become aware of these thoughts and how they are influencing him, and he may be able to do this on his own or he may require help.

His body has also become involved. In particular, the emotion generator and the lower internal regulator set off alarm signals whenever he is close to his wife, particularly when there is the possibility of a sexual encounter. These alarm signals inhibit his sexual performance and render him impotent. All this further compounds his distress and makes him feel even more unsafe, in a space where, of course, he should feel very secure. The personal space around him has become threatening and both his wife and daughters are involved in this. This is, in part, related to the activities of his mind but also, in part, related to the kinds of exchange that occur between him and his wife. Their verbal and physical exchanges have become unproductive and, at times, destructive.

Steven eventually did try to talk things over with his wife and it became clear to them that much of his hostility and feeling of threat was quite unprovoked. However, it also became clear that she was feeling defensive and let down by him and had developed feelings of resentment and anger towards him.

Together they were also able to start talking about the sexual difficulty, although the clear connection between threat and lack of safety and Steven's sexual problem did not become apparent to them until his wife, Carole, had gone to seek some professional help from a women's counselling service. Here again, they were able to help themselves by avoiding intercourse for some weeks and indulging only in sexual exchanges which were not so threatening. Eventually Steven's confidence returned and they were able to resume relationships.

They both also realised that the environment that each provided for the other was far from satisfactory and they resolved to try to change things within their family, to be more complimentary and supportive to each other and less ready to attack with destructive and negative comments. They also involved their daughters in the problem and tried to speak fairly openly and freely about their difficulties.

For all the work they were able to do together, it was quite clear that there were many outstanding problems and after some eight months of partially successful work with each other, Steven had decided, with his wife's agreement, to go into psychotherapy. This is described in some detail now as it illustrates how the safe space of the therapeutic setting allowed Steven to explore more deeply some aspects of himself and his relationships.

In order to face up to and possibly re-experience some of these threatening feelings, Steven needed to share them with a therapist he could trust and to whom he could refer when things got too tough.[6] The safety the therapist provides in these threatening and unknown areas has been likened to that of a seasoned and hardy co-explorer. In this setting not only may difficult and threatening ideas be revealed, but what is concealed and hidden may be sought and, when found, brought out into the safety and privacy of the therapy to be examined. Safety in the therapy does not imply being cushioned or protecting the client against the exploratory steps that you may have to take.

Safety in the psychotherapeutic setting,[6] rather like that in general medical consultation, is of two kinds. Firstly, if the patient is to reveal intimate and perhaps shameful or unacceptable ideas, then they need to feel safe with the person to whom they are revealing. Secondly, the therapy offers an intimate relationship in a controlled setting, so that the patient who has previously been unable to get close to people may feel safe enough to do this in therapy. The patient may actually get very close to the therapist and attached to him or her and then again have to go through the whole performance of loss, of breaking away and becoming independent, which may have been something that he failed to do satisfactorily as a child. Therapy may give him or her a second chance to do this.

As well as the safety of the relationship, there is the pursuit of the hidden and recognised elements of mind that may be contributing. You will recall that the second of Stephen's difficulties was that he could not deal with the problem because he did not really know what it was.

Unconscious ideas often feature things that happened long ago in early childhood or ideas which, if reached, would be damaging to our self-esteem. In the pursuit of them you have to be something of a detective, looking for the things outside that threaten or upset you without any obvious good reason. A pattern may become apparent which may be linked to your past. Try to remember painful episodes in your childhood, any separations from either parent or particular confrontations. This sort of thing may at least set you on the right track. Often you can do some of this on your own or with a trusted friend or partner, although more detailed exploration may require the help of an expert.

On your own or with a therapist or trusted friend you may look at dreams, ideas, thoughts or your own recall of your past for clues. Now many would say the pursuit of unconscious material on your own is very difficult, and that some form of dynamic psychotherapy will be required. In some cases this is true, but overkill is equally common, where some simple and basic unconscious problem leads a person into intensive psychoanalysis that lasts many years, and really may not have been necessary.

In a variety of psychotherapies, the basic principles are similar. The client, perhaps aided by the therapist, tries to identify his or her feelings and to get at the real reasons behind this or that feeling, the historical roots of a particular sensitivity. All this can be very unsettling. Over a period of time a whole structure of logical reasons justifying a particular view of the world or the self may have to be taken apart, examined and put together again.[7] Frequently a set of opinions or values that worked long ago is not discarded and may be clung onto, perhaps to avoid facing some new and threatening reality.

At the start of therapy Steven said, 'My mother was wonderful, she gave me everything I needed', implying that he had only positive feelings for his mother. As the therapy developed it emerged that he and his father were both quite afraid of this wonderful woman. At a deeper level, as a child he felt abandoned and let down and cross with his mother, yet he could never dare say or admit it to himself, and also felt very guilty for even thinking it. The knowledge of all this helped Steven to make more sense of his life and his relationship with his wife and daughters. Working it all out and readjusting his view of himself and his mother, however, was very threatening, and only in a safe but neutral environment with a sensitive and careful therapist could he go through with it, in his own way, and in his own time.

Steven's initial approach was to deny that he had any real problem, for to do that would have been self-indulgent and to admit to weakness. He tried to convince his therapist that it was his wife's problem and that he was fine. Gradually as he became safer in the therapy he was able to allow weakness and neediness in his therapy and then to begin to look back at the denial of all this in his own childhood. The realisation of the true nature of his problem came as something of a revelation to him and at once he was able to begin to make some more changes at home.

Often in the safety of the psychotherapeutic relationship we do not just explore and look for hidden or unconscious reasons. We may also bring into the therapeutic relationship exactly those problems that are upsetting or damaging our relationships in the outside world. Sometimes we may also repeat with the therapist some intricate and complicated relationship that was perhaps unsatisfactory when we first experienced it long ago. Therapy also gives us a chance to have 'another try' at an intimate and close relationship with another human being in a controlled setting.

Therapy is not just about discovering, not just about knowing but also about experiencing. Thus within the therapeutic relationship we may actually re-experience the relationship with mother or father or another key figure,[9] have another go at it, and learn from the second run and try to do it better. And thus, in the relationship with the therapist, we may start to respond as if the therapist were actually our mother, or father or whoever the key person was. To put it in very basic terms, if the early relationship with mother was unsatisfactory and in some way difficult, then as the analytic therapy develops so you may start behaving towards the therapist just as you behave towards your mother. Consider here Steven H.'s response in therapy towards his therapist.

As described earlier on, he blamed his wife for the difficulty and could not even admit that he had any problem or much in the way of *emotional* needs from his marriage. He just wanted respect and courtesy as the father and head of the household. As therapy developed he sought to impress the therapist with his strength and self-reliance and his ability to cope entirely on his own. All this of course was part of the training he had received from his mother. Then gradually, as needy as ever and increasingly frustrated, he began to attack the therapist for failing him and letting him down. This was exactly what he had been doing to his wife, and also what he and his mother had done to his father. Here in therapy he was beginning to re-live his old relationships in a different setting and here in therapy this repetition could be gently shown to him.[9]

It gradually became clear that he was attacking the male therapist, just as he had attacked his father. He could not allow his father to have any good, powerful or strong qualities. He only saw the negative side of him. By putting him down and denigrating him, he deprived himself of any chance of making a strong and firm relationship with him. He felt isolated from men and somewhat hostile, not only towards other men but inwardly critical of himself. As the therapy progressed, however, he started to find some good and positive features in his therapist. He began not only to appreciate him but also to begin to rely upon him. He experienced, within the therapy, the safety of a close relationship with another man. He also began to develop the capacity to forgive other men for failing, at least in part, and from this experience he was able to start forgiving himself for failing, at least in part. All this took some months to go through but it did seem to be extremely helpful to him.

As well as the repetition of past failures in therapy, there is also what has been called by many the 'real relationship', the here and now meeting between two quite separate people. This means that although Steven was patient and the doctor was therapist, they were still people, and there was an irreducible contact between them, in which their personalities, idiosyncrasies, likes, dislikes and so on intruded.[10]

Steven had gone into therapy with a man who was much older than himself. Nevertheless, they had quite a few interests in common and were both especially fond of English music. They also found that they had spent time in Worcester and in the Malvern Hills and were able to discuss various walks that they had taken and to compare notes about some of the interesting footpaths. This real similarity between them allowed them time to step outside the divisions of the therapeutic setting and to meet as people and make real contact.

Steven attended for psychotherapy for one hour a week over a period of about fifteen months. During this time there was a marked improvement in his relationship with his family. He became much less sensitive to attacks on himself, was less guarded and much more open. He began to respect himself more and made allowances for himself, and when his wife was critical of him he did not always take this to heart and feel utterly damned by it. Gradually he began to re-establish links with his wife, just as he had established links with the therapist. He began, once again, to trust and share and to allow himself weakness when he felt weak, but also to enjoy his strength and determination when he felt strong and determined. He was beginning to become a real person, with good and bad, weak and strong and so forth. Gradually the safety and strength of his family life began to fortify him and he began to realise that, as a whole group, they had a great deal to offer each other. Of course there were disagreements, but at the same time there was a lot more tolerance and respect and mutual support.

Psychotherapy is, of course, an intricate and immensely complex matter and very long books have been written about the process. Here, in this short account of Steven's experience,[11,12] some of the rudiments have been introduced. Psychotherapy has also been put into context. It cannot be separated from the personal and intimate environment in which the subject exists. There is no doubt that in Steven's case a change of attitude on the part of his wife and daughters was almost as important as the psychotherapeutic process. Similarly, his impotence was a major problem, but as his home became safe and he began to trust his wife, his sexual function began to improve.

Psychotherapy therefore involves setting up a personal relationship which is safe enough for us to bare our whole self to another person and be known as that whole. It involves often pursuing and discovering hidden and painful things about ourselves and may involve the whole repetition of an early unsatisfactory relationship in the safety of the therapeutic setting.[5,9] Here is contact between person and person, here is meeting. Here you may be known as you really are. All this new intimate experience can be useful in itself but it can also generalise to other external relationships.

At times in our lives we all need a wise guide, an archetypal helper to turn to, a mother figure, a father figure, a saint, guru, mystic or scientist. These figures are beginning to reappear in modern society. Often it is the psychotherapist or counsellor who takes on the role. The care and concern of the therapist may give us the strength to get through a difficult phase.[10] Here is support, here is the attachment, and here some would say is love, which is a great and powerful healer. Here certainly is safety which may be a vital refuge during a great strain. With the flowering of complementary therapies and alternative medicine, a whole new variety of therapeutic techniques are emerging, involving drama, dance or touch. Sometimese these can be more effective or appropriate than psychotherapy.

We are most vulnerable at times of disruption and change, when our safety is shattered and our inner and outer equilibrium is disturbed. At these times we may seek therapeutic help, but which therapy and which therapist? Proceed with care. There are some good powerful positive things around but there are also some bad and negative things around. The wrong therapy with the wrong therapist may be a disaster. Do some research before you commit yourself, do not just take the advice of one friend who had a friend who was helped six years ago. Try to find out more about the therapy and the therapist.

As a general rule, the more unstable you feel the more conservative and careful you should be with your choice of therapy. Choose a method that is well established and which has a good record. Many so-called 'therapies' were originally designed for people who were feeling very stable and who wanted to explore themselves and expand their horizons; they were not designed for people in crisis. These techniques broadly belong to what is called 'the growth movement' and, although some of them may be therapeutic, many of them are inappropriate for people in distress.

Try to find a therapist who has been well recommended and who has undergone a recognised form of training. Do not feel bad about changing your therapist early on if it does not feel right. Working closely with another person is a very intimate matter and it is important that you feel some sense of compatibility and that you feel at ease with them. The sex of the therapist can be very important: if you want somebody of the same sex to help you, then make sure you get somebody of the same sex and the right sort of age. If you are a woman who has been raped, then you will probably do better by discussing all this with another woman. If you are a man having problems with retirement, then you are unlikely to get on very well with a newly qualified young man, although you just might. Do not forget the therapy is for you, not for the therapist, and it is easy to be intimidated or mystified by the whole performance, especially if there is a lot of jargon around. Try to see the therapy for what it is, and set limits to your expectations. It is unlikely to change you or your life completely, or to solve all your problems.

Usually there is a honeymoon period. You spill out all your difficulties and worries that you have been concealing within yourself, perhaps for years. Suddenly you have a safe setting in which you can reveal all this, and almost at once you feel better – you have confided, confessed and made contact. In the early stage there may be no shortage of optimism, then, as the therapy progresses, you may start to find that a lot of it is coming back to you. The therapist is there, dependable, trustworthy and understanding, but the problem outside in the world is still there and you have to face it. Similarly your inner feeling of shyness or anger or insecurity is still there, and you have to try to understand it, sort it out and make some changes with the help of the therapist. but you have to do a lot of work.

The safe space of love is one of the most fundamental requirements of human beings. The capacity to love and trust is closely related to our early childhood experiences and when things go wrong it may sometimes help to go back to our early experiences to try to find the answer. Psychotherapy will offer explanations, a chance to try out a new and intimate relationship in safe conditions and a period of support and possibly love.

On 6 December 1906 Freud wrote to Jung about patients who were unaffected by interpretations of the transference.[13] In one such case he wrote: 'One might say the cure is effected by love.' At times in therapy you may simply find some of the love you need, at other times you will find something more. Whatever the case, the realisation of the need, and the strength to admit to and own up to that need, is a most important step.

10

ILLNESS AND VULNERABILITY

Somewhere within the experience of illness are all kinds of important truths about what it means to be fit and well with a normal sound body, living a reasonable life in fairly acceptable surroundings. How often people say after recovery from an illness or accident: 'I never realised before how wonderful it is simply to be healthy, or simply to be alive' or 'after three months with a full-length plaster on my leg, I am amazed at the pleasure of walking to the shop on the corner to buy a newspaper'.

Ask any hundred people what safety they most cherish and eight-five of them will reply the safety of good health, the safety of freedom from serious illness. There can be few more pronounced losses of safe space than the intrusion of serious illness into our lives. In many instances mysterious and perhaps painful symptoms are experienced as a threat, as a very fundamental and crude disruption of our safe space – of the concrete space of our bodies, the territory within us, and in a wider sense the safe space around us and our ability to function in the world.

For many, illness is the most direct expression of a world that is not as safe as it should be. Illness has become a symbol of our frailty, a symbol of the human condition and an ever present reminder that science and technology certainly cannot do everything. Just as illness has come to express threat and the unknown, so all too often therapy and therapists have taken on all kinds of protective and parental roles.

Although our body is us, it is also experienced as something apart. We may have the feeling of not only being our body but being in it – living in it. Our body may be experienced as a space in which we exist, and so we are very aware of its quality, performance and function. This chapter is not so much concerned with the causes or treatment of illness, but with illness as a condition of our bodies and our experience. Within a strong, fit body, we feel secure. We can enjoy its function and agility, its pleasure and sensuality. It can be a component of various systems, but it is also a space within which things happen.

We expect our bodies to work well and we are surprised and threatened if they do not. All too often, when they do work well, we take them for granted and just get on with our lives, expecting the body to adapt to all kinds of strange foods, irregular hours, long journeys, change in time zones, alcohol, tobacco, drugs and so on. It's as if many of us don't notice our body until it begins to go wrong – but then, all at once, its vital role in our security and stability becomes obvious. Not only are we acutely sensitive to and very threatened by certain kinds of illness, but it is a common finding that damage to some specific parts of the body produces much more insecurity and threat than is the case with other parts.[1,2]

At some very fundamental level we all realise that the body that we are, or that we inhabit, or own, is a structure of the most extraordinary fragility. The principal experience of this is, of course, in our own soft, damp, uncoordinated, immobile babyhood, where we probably don't feel much safer than a thinking jellyfish. As we grow, it is not the development of hard scales or bony armour that gives us strength and security, but the most extraordinary intelligence and canniness, cooperation with others like us, and finally, a battery of extraordinary and often very effective technical and mechanical aids which include everything from clothing to cars, from central heating to antibiotics, from inoculation to machine guns.

Do not lose sight of the sleight of hand in all this. The safety and security ultimately are not us and what we are – they are what we learn and do, and what we might have. These subtle skills depend on good bodies, good minds and good friends, for these material accessories are bought at a price, which is why the rich, and especially those who are rich in rich countries, have more of them and live longer, while the poor, and particularly those in poor countries, have less and live for a shorter time.[3]

The strength, security and safety of adulthood is partly illusion, for consumption by us and more particularly by our children, and the most important cultural lesson is supposed to be that mastery, strength and safety will come with age and will be fulfilled by the collective goals and purposes of the culture. That is the promise. Yet the skin is still soft and bleeds when punctured, the belly still contains guts, and the skull has within it a very soft and vulnerable brain. The sight of the road accident victim or the terminally ill, or the starving mother and child, reaches not only our humanity and its mutual concern, but also our vulnerability. These things remind us that we are not as safe as we would wish to be or believe ourselves to be.

'Insecurity lies at the heart of our reaction to disease: when illness strikes, we feel as if under attack. The defences which have enabled us to ignore our potential for frailty and vulnerability are suddenly removed. We are no longer able to fulfil the social roles which provide us with a sense of identity. Business cannot be "as usual", and instead of being busy, we are slowed down or immoblised and forced to break routines, go to bed, seek help and take stock. We no longer "feel ourselves", as we are confronted with the full force of the unknown and the unpredictable.'[4]

The realisation of this truth can be an important and often vitally stabilising and grounding idea in the face of the cant which endlessly proposes 'man as machine' or 'man as pleasure dome'. Illness is not just damage and destruction, for in its early stages (particularly before irreversible pathological alteration in organ systems) it can serve to guide us and broaden our vision of ourselves[5] and remind us of our true nature, and our need for balance and safety. For all that, our most immediate experience of illness is much less subtle and often seen quite directly as a threat, as something intrusive that strikes right at the centre of our safe space. Let us look a little more closely at how we experience illness and how the experience of it disturbs and threatens our safe space.

In its early stage illness is often experienced as something puzzling, something alien, something not understood. Although much has been written about modern man's excessive preoccupation with the fear of illness, there is much anthropological evidence to suggest that in a wide variety of cultures illness is seen as something dangerous and alien, perhaps instigated by witchcraft, evil eye, bad spirits or as a punishment for wrongdoing. There is a surprising consistency in the way people use a few basic forms of explanation to account for what has gone wrong with their body.[2,6]

Illness is:

(1) seen as the production of degeneration – of the running down of the body;
(2) seen as a mechanical problem, associated with damage or blockage to bodily structures;
(3) associated with imbalance, either of bodily parts and function, or between the individual and the environment;
(4) related to invasion by alien substances or infectious agents.

In most cultures fundamental beliefs about illness may involve one or more of these basic models. Using these, we try to explain what has gone wrong with ourselves, make sense of it and exert some control over it.[7]

The cultural account of course not only shapes the response to the symptom but also will have implications for treatment. Religion, folklore, old remedies, talismen, charms and so on warded off the evil influences that lead to illness, and supposedly made us safe once again. Our society is in a state of very rapid transition. Modern medicine is little more than a hundred years old. It is not surprising that our culture has lost control of its special potent magic and of the guardians of that, the doctors. At times doctors have abused their power, at times they have been misguided, but no more so than those people who complain about medical inadequacy with no constructive attempt to put anything new in its place. The challenge is not to abandon technology but to find a place for it.[8] The challenge is to find a place for a number of the old myths and to write and dream up new ones.

Some of the earliest beliefs about the causes of illness are centred on transgressions of the social mores of the community. Once this had occurred the spirits would act to damage the guilty party, acting through a magic man, a sorcerer or directly. Other causal theories involved the intrusion of some kind of foreign object such as a piece of bone or chip of stone. This might later be extracted in some sort of magic ritual supervised by a magic man or sorcerer.

Good functioning was vitally dependent on the integrity of the soul, and a variety of untoward happenings, such as a fright, a fall or something else, could cause loss of soul which in turn could lead on directly to illness. Even the glance of another person, if that glance intended evil or carried envy or some other desire with it, could disrupt safety and induce illness. Hence a belief in the evil eye which exists to some degree right up to the present day. Many sorts of talismen or amulets were worn to protect against the evil eye.

Because much causal explanation for illness was routed in the supernatural, the fusion of myth, religous belief and medicine readily occurred, and one common culture for any group of people could serve to explain a whole broad span of problems ranging from failed crops to still-birth, from a poisoned finger to sudden death or thunderstorms. Within this system everybody knew where they stood and everybody obeyed the rules. Although the secrets of exorcism, cure and so forth might be enshrined in a magic man or in one or two elders of the tribe, the whole community would participate in a healing activity which was often closely linked to religion. This may well have produced feelings of involvement and control that led to feelings of security and understanding in the face of bodily disorder.

Much illness was seen either as a punishment for sin or as the result of witchcraft or possession. Nowhere was this more brutally manifested than in the field of mental illness, where demonic possession was the standard explanation. Books were written on the recognition of witches and many of the mentally ill were treated as witches and tortured and brutalised. As late as 1593 three witches were hanged at Huntington.

In November 1589 a ten-year-old girl, Jane Frogmorton, suffered an illness characterised by sneezing, shaking and fits. Unfortunately, after an old woman called Alice Samuel visited the sick child, four more children within the same family also soon fell ill with the same disease.

The stricken parents accused Alice Samuel of being a witch. Eventually she, her husband and her daughter Agnes were sent to trial at the Huntington Assizes and subsequently on the basis of confessions the three were found guilty and hanged. Witches were supposedly able to cause injury and damage to people they disliked, even at a distance, often modelling their victims in wax before inflicting disease and destruction upon them.

Witches are no longer cited as causes for disease and have been replaced by rational explanations. Some people argue that disease has actually become more threatening to our sense of safety than it was in the Middle Ages. They attribute this partly to the increasing sense of alienation that we feel in regard to the control of our own health.

Many writers and critics of modern medicine look back to a golden age where each individual or small community was responsible for its own health, within a unifying culture that gave meaning and a sense[9] of cohesion and safety to the population. Ivan Illich writes of the Modern Medical Failure which he calls medical nemesis: 'Medical Nemesis is the experience of people who are largely deprived of any autonomous ability to cope with nature, neighbours and dreams and who are technically maintained within environmental, social and symbolic systems.' He argues that the technical and scientific revolution in medicine and the concentration of medical magic (or power) in the hands of a few, deprived ordinary people of any ability to have any real control over their own health, or even removed any feeling that they had some control.

Others argue that even worse than the loss of control and involvement has been the outlawing of healing, magic, faith and traditional spiritual approaches to illness, which formerly had an important place. Although we often do not understand their mode of action, they allowed us to muster all our natural and inbuilt healing power to fight disease and disorder.

The only response to the threat of illness (illness and death were of course seen as increasingly alien) was to run for help to men with power who although sometimes potent, often could not be understood and demanded complete passivity from the patient. Disease became something to be feared, because in part it involved complete loss of mastery, loss of control and separation from home, family and friends.

In the last fifteen or twenty years there has been a growing movement to make health once again an integral part of common and personal culture and to get more cooperation between the medical establishment and the consumers of medicine. The rising interest in diet, exercise, sexuality and childbirth is all evidence of this, as is the enormous variety of self-help and pressure groups that exist in relation to almost every kind of disease and disorder. The provision of medical care is becoming ever more expensive and technical procedures that may prolong a single life for a short period cost very large sums of money. How these resources are to be allocated is an increasingly difficult problem. We are once again becoming actively involved in discussion about our own health and our own illness. Perhaps a new culture of medicine is about to be born. Fortunately, not all doctors are power crazy, committed to medical monopoly and deprived of the power of communication.

The middle ground that will make illness safer involves:

(1) A better understanding of the business of being ill and being well.
(2) Insisting on good communication between those who control and administer health resources and those who consume them, asking what is going on, trying to get involved in treatment choices, joining self-help groups.

(3) Taking an active interest in maintaining your health and the health of those you love and care about – this is a basic right.

(4) Remembering who and what we are. There is no paradise on earth. We must all get ill from time to time, all of us are getting older every day, one day when we are old we will die. That is part of life.

Each of us when ill may 'explain' our disorder at a variety of levels. We may know all about the scientific account or the biology, but at the same time may inwardly hang onto some other deeper, more 'primitive' or 'personal' account. We may know that the symptoms are caused by a virus but wonder inwardly 'why did I get this infection at this time, what did I do? What kind of imbalance is there in my body to make me vulnerable to this?'[10]

Along with our ideas of cause existing at different levels there will also be our own picture of what is happening inside us. We may be told there is a 'small blood clot blocking an artery' but if asked to 'get an image of what is going on' we may visualise something very different from what the pathologist would see through his microscope. Within the personal meaning of illness we may think of personal models of cause, such as why this happened to me at this time, and also personal models of pathology, wondering what is going on in my body.

One useful way of looking at all this is to consider the problem in two ways. There is the technical description and there is the personal experience. These are two aspects of the problem – the disease from which you are suffering, and the illness which you are experiencing. The disease is the physical process that is causing the trouble, the broken bone, the virus that causes the common cold, the slipped disc that presses on the nerve. The illness is the sum total of what is going on for you – how it feels, how it disrupts your life, your unique personal experience of a particular disease.

When you go to your doctor you want to know all about the disease and its effects and you want the best treatment, but you also may want to present some of your illness experience and get help with that.[11,12] Consider this in relation to cystitis, a disease in which bacteria infect the bladder. The mainstay of treatment lies in antibiotics (tetracycline) or sulphonamide drugs (cotrimoxazole) which interfere with the metabolic processes of the bacteria. Before giving such drugs, it may be necessary to culture some of the urine in a laboratory and grow the infecting organisms on a plate of agar gel to see which drugs the bacteria are sensitive to. All this is technical and based on science.

By contrast, the personal experience of your 'illness' is somewhat different. If you have cystitis you are likely to have pain and discomfort in your lower abdomen, you may have to pass urine frequently and it is likely to burn and sting. If you have never had it before you may worry about the diagnosis. 'Is it cancer or venereal disease? If it is cancer will it be fatal? If it is venereal disease from whom did I catch it, or to whom have I given it?' Perhaps somebody in your family had some similar disorder and was very ill with it, so these symptoms may have particular significance for you. Perhaps you had bedwetting problems as a child so you may be very sensitive about your bladder and matters connected with urine. Your performance at work may be upset and your sleep impaired. You may be feeling ashamed, anxious, confused and certainly unsafe. What are you going to do? How are you going to sort it out? Dare you tell a friend? If it is venereal disease, how would your doctor respond? What would you say to your wife or husband?

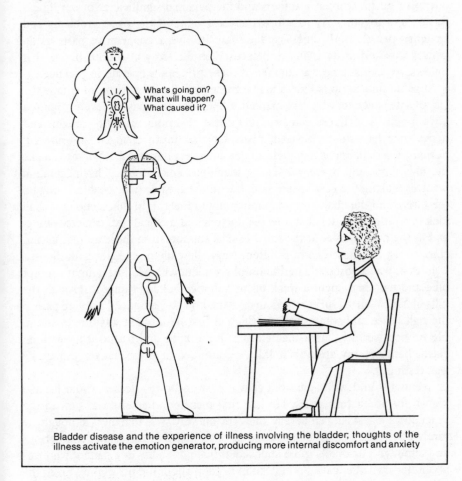

Bladder disease and the experience of illness involving the bladder; thoughts of the illness activate the emotion generator, producing more internal discomfort and anxiety

This sort of sequence often goes with the experience of even the most basic symptoms. It is clear that the insecurity and emotion generated by these doubts and worries may become so intrusive and pervasive as to make the original symptoms of almost secondary importance. The worry may, in turn, actually influence the progress of the disease. Feeling helpless, demoralised, guilty and anxious will lessen your ability to fight the disorder. The body's (your) natural defences will be less effective, and stress and fatigue will aggravate the disorder. It is clear that the problems of illness require more than just good scientific treatment – although, of course, that is an essential first step. Rational effective scientific medicine is a very expensive and very new commodity, but few of us suffering serious illness would choose to dispense with it.

Illness requires something additional, it requires that we work with the doctor or health worker to understand the personal significance of our illness for us, and together try to address at least some of the basic problems and anxieties posed. Both illness and disease involve a cooperative partnership between us and those trying to help us.[13] In the story of serious illness that follows, we can see how a number of these principles operate in practice.

At some time serious illness may intrude into our lives. Here of course the loss of safe space may be very marked. All at once you may be severely limited in your activities. There may be a real threat of serious disability, dreams and hopes may have to be revised, plans for the future changed and altered. Serious illness happens to people all day and every day and most of them make the most amazing, brave, tenacious, ingenious adaptations. That adaptation involves making the very unsafe safe, the unmanageable manageable, sizing up the threat and the challenge and attempting to meet it. In this section we shall look in a little more detail at how the doctors and medical staff can contribute, and in the next chapter at the role of social support from those around us and close to us. All these can in different ways allow us to get safer with illness.

John F. was a postgraduate Philosophy student who had just bought a motor bike and who had spent a week of his summer holiday riding it through the hills of Mid Wales. During the course of the holiday he noticed a severe pain in the right knee and some swelling which at first he thought was due to strain. He rubbed various patent medicines into the knee and bound it up with an elastic bandage, but after his holiday it continued to give pain even though he was resting it.

Eventually and with some reluctance he went to his doctor whom he had known for about four years. He had first met her when she was new in the practice as a trainee. Generally they got on very well together, although he rarely consulted her. She suspected at once that this was something serious and although personally quite shocked at this possibility in a patient who was about her own age, gave no indication to John about the possibility. From the start she considered the likelihood of malignancy, and as if to warn him said that she thought it might be more serious than it looked and that he ought to go and have an X-ray and some blood tests.

Although John F. had felt safe and at ease with his doctor he felt very unsafe by the time he went to bed that night after the consultation. What seemed to be a sprained knee was now looking quite sinister.

The X-ray revealed without any doubt a malignant tumour. It seemed to have been present for some time, but clearly produced no symptoms. Such tumours of bone are quite rare, but there was some research work to suggest that exposure to ionising radiation increased your risk of developing such tumours. As with many tumours induced by radioactivity, the time-lag may be considerable, so that it's all too easy to play down or even forget the causal association.

When the lack of safe space is obvious, as in fire or flood, the danger is easy to recognise. Rapidly acting infections, such as those acquired from contaminated food and water, are also easy to appreciate, but the nuclear risk is particularly sinister because in low doses the effects are very difficult to appreciate. Many of these effects will only be felt by the next and unborn generation through genetic defects, or there may be no significant change until a tumour appears after the lag of say ten or even twenty years.

John had a special relationship with nuclear power and activity. His father was a scientist who had been seconded to the American Navy and was on a destroyer near Bikini Atoll when the USA detonated its first hydrogen bomb codenamed 'Castle Bravo' on 1 March 1954. The destroyer, with John's father on it – and the same thing happened to a nearby Japanese fishing boat – was showered with atomic fallout. Later, when John's father returned to England, he and the family settled near Windscale (now called Sellafield) to continue his work on nuclear power. Two years later John was born.

John was very successful at school, took a good degree in physics and, like his father, went into the nuclear industry. At the age of twenty-eight, worried about the increasing risks of nuclear waste disposal, he decided to go back to university to write a thesis on the subject.

What had caused John's tumour? The doctors were aware of his family background. His father had been exposed to radiation at the Marshall Islands – could this be a late genetic effect? John had grown up close to Windscale, breathed the air, drunk the local milk and later worked in the nuclear industry and even conducted experiments in the laboratory with radioactive materials. Was it possible that somewhere along the line the spaces in which John lived had just not been materially safe enough, and the tumour was the result?

If John was to have a good chance of survival, his right leg would have to be removed above the knee. The doctor discussed the X-rays with the orthopaedic surgeon and decided that as she knew him well and they wanted to avoid painful delay, she should break the news to him. In doing this she tried to be truthful, respecting the person and his integrity, and avoided telling him more than he could take.[1] To make this kind of judgement she of course had to have some grasp of him as a person and an understanding of his make-up.

When he came in for the X-ray result he showed a certain bravado, flippantly saying, 'I've written to the bike manufacturer asking for my money back'. The doctor, inwardly bracing herself and trying to think of him rather than herself, told him: 'As I think you suspected, the X-ray does show some serious disorder. There is a growth there and you will have to see a specialist and I think you may have to go into hospital for an operation.'

There were no lies here, but the doctor was giving him plenty of scope to get as much or as little information as he wanted. He clearly looked shaken but did not press to know what kind of tumour and what kind of operation. It was only the next day when he saw the surgeon that the shock really hit him. He felt stunned, he felt as if his whole world was falling apart.

Over the next few days or so he staged a remarkable come-back, stopping all his work, seeing friends, drinking a lot and becoming careless with his money. He was now in the stage of denial – it can't happen to me, it can't be true. At some level he may have known, but he could not take it. The reality was too shattering, too unsafe, so he preferred make-believe whereby the threat would be forgotten.

The day before he was due to go into hospital, however, fear and anxiety began to creep up on him. He felt that no matter how fast he ran, the fear would stay with him. He felt desperately alone, he needed somebody to be with, somebody to talk to. He phoned the doctor and she agreed to see him at the end of her evening surgery. She had made her technical contribution in the diagnosis and tests, now she had to continue with her more humane and personal contribution. She let him talk and when he wanted more information she gave it to him. By the end of the discussion he was still tense but was beginning to build up a realistic picture of the threat and what he had to cope with. He was beginning to prepare himself, and although he was tense and sad, his feelings were appropriate to what was going on. He could begin to see the danger and the threat as it really was.[14]

In the post-operative week he was quite depressed but resigned to what had happened, he was beginning to accept it. He met a group of patients who had made a successful recovery from the operation and talked with them about getting used to an artificial limb and trying to make the most of it. What had been a vast and limitless threat was beginning to get a shape and boundaries. He was feeling a little safer with this very unsafe situation. It is important to note here that in facing something like an operation or tooth extraction which is clearly a real threat to safety, some realistic preparation beforehand improves coping. Patients who are worried about the unpleasant effects of surgery[15] do better post-operatively than those who do not.

Over the following six months John F. saw his doctor every two weeks to talk over his problem. He now felt very obliged to her and very warm and, in an ironic way, grateful. She had saved his life and was a figure of power and authority to whom he could turn. She liked him and was really concerned about his progress, but she was also careful not to feel too flattered or gratified by his dependence on her or by his liking for her. At times when he cried she would put a hand on his shoulder but was always careful, within the safe and trusting relationship, gently to coax him into taking control of his own life. If through guilt or a sense of personal gratification she encouraged his dependence to excess, he might retreat into a child-like position and let her be his parent who 'would make everything OK for him'.

Gradually over the next year he began to make an adaption to his circumstances. He returned to his studies, started writing his thesis and began to see all his old friends.

Now it is clear that this serious and difficult problem is not solved simply by providing initial safety or facilitating the development of safety and coping in the face of serious threat. All kinds of very intricate adaptations are involved, but many of them can be seen in relation to the development of a view of life that makes everything manageable once again and, to some degree, rewarding and personally meaningful. What was a pervasive threat intruding into every aspect of John's life was gradually given shape and form and sense, so that whole areas of life gradually became safe again, possible again, rewarding again. Of course some threat remains, but John even begins to feel safe with the threat, for he begins to define its boundaries and to know exactly what it entails.

The apparently unbridgeable gap between the doctor's technical and clinical approach and the patient's personal experience is ironically bridged in one particular situation – where the doctor suffers a serious illness and finds himself or herself on the other side of the consulting room table. In September 1982 Dr Vicky Clement-Jones, who was a research fellow at St Bartholomew's Hospital in London, was found to have cancer. Her experience of this disorder and its subsequent successful treatment led her to form a new association which specialises in providing information and encouraging support for cancer patients and their relatives. She describes in great detail, both from the medical point of view and her personal one, what it was like to have a disease with little hope of survival. She told the story of her experience in a Paper published in the *British Medical Journal*.[16] It makes very moving reading and tells us a great deal about the threatening and insecure world of cancer, about the enormous resilience of human beings and the way in which the unknown and the unsafe can be made less threatening.

She describes how, after the diagnosis, she felt her world was completely shattered, and how she was overcome by numbness and sadness. Both she and her husband thought it unlikely that she would survive, even for three months, and they feared that she would not see another Christmas. It was only following the visit of a medical oncologist who offered to treat her with cytotoxic chemotherapy that she suddenly realised there was some hope. What had been an unknown, limitless threat began to assume more manageable proportions.

Because the tumor was inoperable, her only hope of cure was through chemotherapy. This treatment was demanding, physically debilitating and full of additional hazards such as loss of hair, vomiting and weakness. Although her doctor was able to explain some of this, Dr Clement-Jones describes in her paper how, in addition to the excellent medical support and information she received, something much more subtle was required to complement this.

That elusive additional ingredient is very much to do with other people. The threat that she faced in the beginning was unknown and limitless, and she could do very little other than submit herself to medical technology, having no idea how to get through the ordeal that faced her. The situation could not have been more unsafe. What was needed was somehow to give shape to the beast, to describe its characteristics and to begin to make sense of it. She had to fight and to overcome, and in order to do this she needed knowledge, experience and comradeship. This she achieved through contact with other people who had undergone chemotherapy. They had been there, they had fought the beast. They knew just what it was like the day after an injection of cytotoxic drugs. In sharing with other people who had fought the same fight she found a new strength.

She tells how, as a doctor, she was privileged to be given access to a single side room, and she goes on: 'When I went for surgery to the gynaecological ward I finally met a fellow young patient with ovarian cancer. We shared our experience of chemotherapy, anticipatory vomiting, the trauma of repeated venopuncture with ever vanishing veins, the loss of childbearing and the onset of menopausal hot flushes, and in this way we supported each other through these difficult times. Through this experience I realised that other patients could give me something unique which I could not obtain from my doctors or nurses, however caring.'

Initially her contact with other patients was informal, but later on she attended two cancer support groups which involved patients, relatives, friends, doctors and nurses.

The skill, dedication and commitment of the doctors and nurses who looked after her, combined with her own determination and the support of those around her, have enabled Vicky Clement-Jones to make a recovery. She is now absolutely committed to passing on the lessons she has learned both to other patients and to the medical profession. In concluding her paper she emphasises how important it is to meet people who have been 'on the inside', and to receive as much information as is required, for both patients and relatives. She stresses the need to become involved and to try to regain control in a situation which initially seems to be out of control.

Increasing acceptance of a dual approach, recognising both the general technical problems posed by disease and the more particular personal troubles posed by illness, has led to the formation of many similar groups. There have never been more self-help organisations and pressure groups designed to cater for the special needs of particular patients. These groups cover almost every disease from asthma to AIDS (for the latter, the Terence Higgins Trust).

They include rare diseases such as phenylketonuria and cystic fibrosis, and also seek to help patients who have had particular kinds of operations such as laryngectomy and colostomy.

These organisations and groups are all involved in the recognition of the wider and often non-material aspects of disease – the way disease alters the quality of both space and function of the body, requiring new perceptions of ourselves and adjustments of our self-esteem. They are concerned with the way disease inhibits our involvement in a whole variety of social and personal functional systems, perhaps preventing or restricting work or social life or interplay with family roles and sexual relationships.

To us as patients illness is at first something to overcome. To do this we need allies, support, cure and healing. The disease is a threat and a disruption of our safety, but many diseases deserve a second look, for although they may threaten us and distress us, they also may say something very important about ourselves or our relationship with our environment, often indicating that the balance between us and our environment has become disturbed.

In disease we may rediscover not only the safety that we derive from the normal function of our own body, but also the safety that we can derive from the support and care of those around us.

11

LIVING LINKS

Without the Joneses, with whom would we keep up? Without the boy or girl next door, with whom would we fall in love? Where would we find someone to feed the cat and water the plants when we're away, someone to gossip with, someone to go to the pub with, someone to tell casually about your promotion or your new posting to Fiji or Surbiton or the Sahara?

Friends, neighbours and workmates are all part of the living links that we make with the world – for better, for worse and for something in between. With them we form a variety of social systems that operate in society with varying degrees of autonomy. We are components of these systems but, at the same time, the systems provide us with spaces within which we operate as individuals. As components we contribute to the whole, but that whole is an environment or space within which we may function as individuals.

Our links and relationships with those around us supply not only material commodities such as security or safety, food, supplies, power and a variety of cultural inputs, but also affection, recognition, acceptance and support.[1]

At the start, the blob of living cells that is to become us is within the mother and linked to the mother's metabolic system. At birth, with the beginnings of independence, we leave the very safe space of the womb to begin to live apart. Yet we are still close, fed from the breast, and very protected by mother and the family. As we grow we gradually develop closer attachments to peers and friends. Later still, in our later teens or early twenties, the family ties weaken and we may develop new very close attachments (such as marriage or a stable loving relationship) which may last for many years, or even till we die.

That delicate balance between dependence and independence, between linkage and separateness, is one that we strive to maintain all through our lives, and although we may choose or have to face a variety of risks, many of us will always seek to return to people and places that support and sustain us. It is all too easy to forget just how important these social links are, for our welfare, health and happiness. For many animal species, group living confers a whole variety of benefits not available to the lone creature. Safety from predators and competing groups of the same species, more effective feeding, safety for the young and shared care of them are just some of the benefits seen not only in the higher mammals like us such as monkeys, but in fish, birds and wild dogs.[2]

It is all too easy to think of relationships as something to do with amusement and stimulation and passing the time, but they do something much more important than that, just as happens with animals. They provide us with a living human network that gives us material and emotional safety. The solitary self-indulgence of a high-fibre diet or the feeling of release at aerobics sessions – with all their hype and hysteria – are no match for a strong supportive group of friends.[3,4]

Because group life has been integral to our survival over millions of years, we have developed a whole variety of complex personality characteristics adapted to that group life. Yet this community life and group support anticipated by evolution has, in a hundred years, been seriously eroded for whole groups in our society, particularly the poor, the unemployed, the mentally ill and the old. Many have simply become numbers on the census form. The neighbours nobody talks to, the strange unnamed person along the corridor, the blank face on the train, whose gaze we avoid.

We are creating a society of sons who never see their mothers, of daughters who have forgotten their fathers. In our strange arrogance, we aspire to self-sufficiency – we don't need other people, they are not good enough for us, they are not worth the effort. Isolation breeds loneliness, alienation and anger. Whole groups who live within society, but lack any personal link with it, are really outsiders.

We have already looked in detail at the rather private links and supports provided by marriage. These cannot take the place of society outside which, through neighbours, work and friendship, complements marriage and certainly can sustain and strengthen marriage and family. Work and employment provide links to other people and contribute considerably to self-esteem. For men in their forties and fifties work is a major source of friendship. A recent study[5] followed the health of a group of workers in England before and after they lost their jobs. Prior to redundancy the rate of consultations with the general practitioner started to rise and with the onset of unemployment, it was found that the group showed a 20 per cent increase in consultations with the family doctor and 60 per cent more visits to the hospital. This accords with other studies which have shown that having a job is associated with mental and physical well being,[6] particularly in women,[7] where outside employment makes them better able to resist stress and pressure.

There are many different kinds of relationship at work. In general those occupying jobs with less skill and less pay are more likely to pursue and enjoy warm supportive contact with their workmates in contrast to the high-flying ambitious executive, who is often rather isolated and, despite outward bonhomie, is often locked into an increasingly desperate battle with his contemporaries which becomes ever more demanding as he rises up the ladder.

Much friendship, of course, has nothing to do with work and is specially important for the younger, older and unemployed.[3] In friendship the ability to be open and honest about oneself with the friends, and to feel safe doing so, seems to be particularly important. We need to be able to trust our friends as well as just to enjoy pleasant and satisfying contact with them.[3]

Jane G., a clinical psychologist in a unit for children with severe learning difficulties, was married to a psychologist whom she had met at university. He was rather mathematical in his approach and has gone on to specialise in some rather obscure research on computer simulation studies of human decision making. The marriage was childless by mutual agreement and they devoted much of their joint income and energy to their home, to sport and to travelling abroad at least twice a year.

They loved each other, initially had similar interests and were sexually compatible. After a few years, Jane found that when they were not doing things together or discussing activities or projects, there was something of an empty space in the marriage and in her life. Her husband Peter, although he would not admit it, didn't really like any expression of doubt, difference or uncertainty, or any personal or deep feelings. Jane realised that when she was younger and close to her mother, she had been rather glad of this coolness in the marriage and had collaborated to sustain it. Now her mother was older and lived some distance from her, Jane became increasingly aware of something missing in her life. She loved Peter and was happy with him, but she had nowhere to go, nowhere to hide, nowhere to admit fragility or doubt. No sanctuary, no safe place. Peter was on a speed boat and he wanted another crew member. For Jane there were things other than that. She began to feel lonely and isolated and miserable. She began to lose her sense of purpose and her optimism. She tried out a variety of ways to change him but none moved him. He became resentful in response to her pressure and didn't really understand what was wrong, even when she tried to explain.

Eventually Jane confided in another school friend, even though she found this very difficult, for in so many ways Jane was just like her husband and had been attracted to him because of that. The school friend seemed to be absorbed and interested by what she said and quite surprised Jane by going on to reveal some of her own struggles at work with a male subordinate, who worked under her and who was very resentful of her authority and seniority. Over a two-year period, the two of them met on a fairly regular basis and Jane found herself increasingly glad of the receptive, warm company that her close friend provided. She felt more secure, she worried less and her intermittent feelings of loneliness lessened. Her rediscovery of intimacy helped her to change things within the marriage and she found relations between her and Peter much improved.

Jane's story is important because it shows how a failure of the right linkages or relationships can cause adverse effects. It also reminds us that very often a marriage does have its deficiencies but these can so often be remedied through proper involvement with family, friends and work, but that expecting too much from one person – your spouse – can often lead to difficulties in a relationship. Few people have perfect marriages, although many people have 'good enough' marriages. Marriage or intimate relationships only contribute part of the safe and sustaining space which we need for 'good enough' lives.

Jane's story carries another message. Reading it, we are not at all surprised that Jane's life was much improved by a friend, and we are also not at all surprised by her choosing a woman, a friend of the same sex. The extraordinary thing is that for either sex, it is the company of female friends that most effectively abolishes loneliness[8] – friendship with men does not do this nearly so effectively. David, the King of the Jews, who was devoted to Jonathan, took a different view when he said the friendship of men surpasses the love of women. We shall return to the idea of same sex comradeship in the next chapter, but let us stay with women for a moment.

> It has been repeatedly found that men and women see friendship differently. Women value intimate confidential relationships, with a high level of self-disclosure, affection and social support. Men think that it is important to do things and have fun. Women have a greater number of intimate friendships, mainly with other women; men have friendships which are less intimate, often with married couples.[3]

Friends are united to us not just by shared place or common interest, but also by shared time. We can share with them the changes and intricacies of our life across time. 'She knew me when I weighed eighteen stone.' 'He and I were in prison together for six years.' 'I remember him before he bought the electric razor company.' All that is somehow very reassuring – someone who has been there with us and someone who will stay with us.

We may think of our lives as a journey, in which the significant movement is in the fourth dimension of time, rather than in space. We can map out our own journey in stages: babyhood, childhood, adolescence, adulthood and so on.[4]

Across the time span of a single life, the landscape through which we pass will alter dramatically and some of our travelling companions will change. At different stages there will be different challenges and demands. Those with whom we travel through life have been likened by some to a convoy. This emphasises the ideal of travelling and travelling companions, but the journey, of course, is through time and through life history. At different points in time, a person's convoy will be very different.[4] Consider this example of a woman's convoy at the age of thirty-five and then at the age of seventy-five.

At the age of thirty-five, she still has with her many friends from her childhood, her mother and father as well as her own husband and a variety of friends. At seventy-five she has lost her husband and many childhood friends, but new links have developed and her son and daughter are now important members of her convoy.

In some rural communities where mobility is restricted and family members stay under one roof, even when they marry, the idea of a convoy is a much more real and tangible experience. Within your home and village are all the people with whom you will travel through life, and the linkages and roles are well defined. There is a sense of belonging, of place, of safety that is so pervasive that you hardly notice it, rather like air, which is here and which sustains you all through your life. By contrast, many of us are free from these close links. We have the promise of endless mobility, career success, self-expression, personal growth, transient intimacy and a whole variety of thrills – qualities all highly prized by our culture. The price that many eventually have to pay for all this is uncertainty and isolation and loneliness.

At times of triumph and excitement this isolation can be invigorating, but at times of illness, frailty, economic collapse, marital break-up or old age, it can be nothing short of disastrous. Our humanity will always make its demands, in spite of our ambitions, our dreams and our bribes. Unlike the Zulu men who go off into the bush to kill a lion and then return to take up a new place in their society of origin, all too often we go off, not knowing what to kill, how to kill it and where to go after we've killed it. As Siegfried Sassoon put it: 'Everyone is interested in the winner of the race until the race is over and then they are interested in the winner of the next one'.[9]

It's not just the 'thrill crazy', the adventurous and the ambitious who are without convoys, for there is another major set of obstacles that severely limit our capacity and ability to be part of a network or convoy. Those obstacles may be described, in the broadest sense, as 'personal disability' – so that sadly and ironically it is often those who are most in need of friends and networks or convoys who find themselves without them.

The disadvantage may manifest in a variety of ways. Not only are the blind, disabled and ill affected, but also those who lack the skills that are necessary to communicate rewardingly and effectively with potential friends and group members. The presence of these disadvantages adds greatly to loneliness – or to put it another way, those who are disadvantaged are often lonely. Other common features found in lonely people are a reluctance to be revealing about themselves, a lack of interest in others and a lack of trust. They may also fail to grasp ideas of concern, loyalty and commitment, which are vital contributions to the safety that friendship and convoys give.[4]

Ruth F. was a widowed, retired headmistress. The daughter of a naval officer, she had been brought up to think of herself as 'not like those people next door'. In spite of her education, the idea that she was rather better than others was one that she clung on to, particularly when things became difficult. The more she felt in need, the more she would say to herself, 'But they couldn't help, they're not good enough'.

Fortunately, she was quite religious and as retirement and widowhood cut her living links, her faith increased and she started to involve herself in helping others. At the church and the local old people's home she began to meet other people like herself and, although all her early training encouraged her to reject them, her christianity whispered messages of love and acceptance and forgiveness – which fortunately she listened to. She started to meet other women and to spend time with them. She found that people who were not supposed to be as good as her were, in fact, very good for her. Soon her links with a whole variety of new people began to develop with very tangible benefits.

A survey in 1982[10] – and it is typical of many Western countries – found loneliness in about 20 per cent of people over 65, and about 20 per cent of people between 15 and 24. The widowed or divorced were particularly at risk, with 36 per cent and 29 per cent respectively, reporting loneliness. This was most painful and unpleasant when the space around was not safe, such as during illness, when amongst a crowd of strange people, or following the death of a close relative or friend or at Christmas time. Feeling lonely is also associated with depression, unhappiness and low self-esteem, and with an earlier death from a variety of causes.[3,11,12] The elderly are particularly vulnerable and even when they are faced with a whole variety of difficulties and social problems, the presence of a close, confiding relationship has a marked protective effect. Here in the confidant, it seems there is safety and trust and the promise of help. Where these are absent, depression will often ensue.[13]

Convoys and networks are in fact supportive social systems that can be described rather like material structures. The things that we receive from our involvement in these systems can be thought of in a rather more concrete way, almost as supplies or commodities. A sustaining social system provides us with social support which enables us not only to manage ordinary day to day living, but to deal with the knocks, crises and pain of life. Social support provides four kinds of commodity:

(1) Affection
(2) Affirmation
(3) Assessment
(4) Aid

In the ideal world, this will be exchanged as part of a mutually sustaining system. You give all this to others and you also receive it from them.[1,4]

Let us take each supply in turn and see how it contributes to safe space.

(1) Affection

We have looked at the idea of closeness to one another and the special safety provided by that in an earlier chapter. Affection is a scaled down version of love, but often every bit as important. Feeling another's affection for us, we are aware of their recognition, understanding and acceptance of us and their readiness to be committed to us, especially when times are difficult (ill health, financial difficulties, isolation, old age and so on). We are also aware and fairly assured of their interest, commitment and care. Affection is generally reciprocal or mutual.

(2) Affirmation

Those who love and care for us and know us can remind us in the face of criticism that we are not all bad, or even that the criticism may be generally unfounded. 'The boss may not think much of me but think of all the other people who've known me for twenty-five years and think very differently of me, they affirm my value and worth.' Affirmation can assure us that we have value in a variety of settings and in a variety of ways.

(3) Assessment

There are many problems facing us that often require a second look. We need to stand back and take stock and advice, and the ideas of others are often very welcome at such times. Consider at work how some critical attack or adverse comment often throws us off balance. By turning to friends, family or colleagues we can ask, 'What do you think is going on? Is it really so serious? Are these criticisms justified? What is the motivation for the attack?' The outsider's view, especially from someone at work who understands the situation, may give a completely new view of the situation and make us more able to respond appropriately.

(4) Aid

This element of support must never be forgotten. Real problems often require real action. Usually it is no good just sitting in your chair thinking the problem away – you may need to do something. Real assistance may come from those closest to you or even from a professional (secondary support). Social support is real. It's not just something that we get from professionals, doctors, therapists or counsellors.[14,15] It is something that each one of us is able to give to others and should be able to get from others. How can we understand social support better, link it up to our own minds and bodies and apply it to problems in our daily lives?

Let us say that you become aware of critical comments about you at your place of work. The critical comment may be given in some veiled form, perhaps through gossip, or it may come through a memo. It may come from somebody who is by nature aggressive and possibly has some bad feelings towards you. As soon as you become aware of it the information processor starts to analyse it – What is going on? What have I done wrong? What is going to happen? The processor also starts sorting through all the past memories and records to see if what has been said links in to similar past experiences. 'Perhaps I really am no good, this is just what happened at school.'

Now it is quite clear that this criticism is a threat, it is 'alarming'. You may start to feel unwanted, rejected and alone and wonder if you will be sacked. The emotional generator will begin to respond by setting off some minor alarm signals. Some will register in your mind a feeling of mild fear or anxiety. Some will start to get to your body via the internal regulator. All this makes the heart beat faster and gives you an empty feeling in the pit of the stomach. This sequence in which lack of safety in the outside world is registered and analysed in the mind and then expressed in bodily changes is very like that described in Chapter 4.

Shortly after this when you hear that your job really is in danger, these negative ideas and your own feelings that you are no good may well intensify, and at the same time the bodily symptoms of alarm will also intensify, with the heart racing, feelings of sickness and so on. If this stress continues for a long time it may also aggravate certain kinds of pre-existing physical disorder.[12,16] There may be a recurrence of arthritis, or some other disorder that can be triggered off by the stress response, a return of ulcer symptoms, colitis, stiff neck, high blood pressure or angina. As well as this there may be emotional feelings of fear and despair, with perhaps poor sleep and loss of energy. Taken overall, not only does the space outside feel unsafe, but your inner bodily space has also changed – your safe space is disturbed and you need to restore to it some kind of safety and equilibrium.

The original criticism has now produced three major categories of problem:

(1) The original critical comment from the material and personal space, and the real possibility that your job is under threat.
(2) Your thoughts and worries about this.
(3) Your bodily alarm responses, possibly with associated symptoms of pre-existing disorder, that dominates your bodily space.

Here then is a problem. You have worked out why you have been feeling uncomfortable at work, why you are sleeping badly, why you are feeling a bit tense and stressed. You realise that something is wrong and you are going to set out to master the problem, to do something about it, to sort it out, and to try and make an adjustment.

(1) Assessment

Although you are aware that there is a problem, it is very important to look more carefully at its finer points. Who is criticising you and what are their motives, is there any basis to the criticism in reality? Or is it perhaps nothing more serious than making some minor adjustment to your work practices and invalidating the criticism? If somebody notes that you tend to arrive ten or fifteen minutes late for work and that this is causing resentment, it might be no bad thing to start turning up on time, or even ten minutes early and being rather ostentatious about it so that everybody sees how keen and committed you are. Real criticism can be an important feedback mechanism and it is very important that in the course of assessment you do not take up some sort of self-righteous attitude and say there is never anything wrong with you, you are without fault. This can only aggravate the problem and may do harm in the long term.

Who is making the criticism, do they have some sinister motive, are they involved in some plot to oust you, can you outflank them, can you call in different allies at work who may be able to help you?

In making your assessment you will need to speak to friends, colleagues and so on. Here your convoy is going to make a vital contribution. If you have close allies at work, then you will want to bring them into your confidence and try and discuss the matter with them.

(2) Affection and affirmation

Although we all have a good deal of self-sufficiency and a fairly reasonable concept of ourselves and our worth, when we are under pressure we may have doubts or worries about this and at such times it is always useful to be able to turn to a friend and say, 'Look, do you really think I am doing a good job?' Or perhaps even to present the original criticism to them: 'My deputy on the floor has been spreading rumours about me and implies that I am always turning up late for work and going off early.' A close friend or colleague may be able to affirm your worth in spite of all this: 'Look, you know you do a good job, you know you are liked by your friends, you know the company values your service' and so on. All this affirmation can remind you that even though there may be negative qualities and negative features about you, there are a number of positive and important things about you that make you a valued member of your group.

Beyond this affection exists something unqualified, an affection that says, 'I like you no matter what you are like, I value you no matter how late you get into the office'. Affection often comes from those quite outside the problem situation. In particular, close family or close friends will provide affection which often acts to counteract these negative criticisms.

(3) Aid

When faced with some sort of threat or problem, you may need real help. You may have to borrow a car, borrow some money, go to see a doctor, get some extra tuition in some particular problem area, or whatever. Aid often comes from members of the convoy, for we help each other in times of difficulty and this help may be real, concrete, technical help. In this case an old friend in the organisation is able to get more information for you. You go to the head of your section and enlist his support. He is able to reassure you and give you his full backing. Your convoy has provided you with real help at an important time. Convoy members may be professionals, doctors, social workers, counsellors and so on, and their contribution is often absolutely vital and if used judiciously is an entirely normal and reasonable part of everyday adaptation.

Effective social support can affect our response to threat, both at the higher conscious level and also at the lower emotion generator and bodily regulation levels where threat and alarm may be associated with a whole variety of changes. All this was described in some detail in Chapter 5. We saw how steroid and adrenalin hormones produce these changes. Social support, love, safety and friendship can buffer or reduce threat and so can actually diminish the associated hormonal responses and thus protect the body against the long-term damage associated with them. In a world dazzled by technology the strength and safety provided by living links with other people remains an essential component of our lives.

Our groups do much more than just operate as collections of people who give safety to each other. They are characterised not only by mutual respect and recognition, but by something much more elusive and specially human. In general, not only do groups have a degree of common purpose but group members frequently share quite intricate belief systems and values – all the people in a church or temple believe in the same God and are agreed about how to worship or share similar spiritual experience.

Now this matter of common belief is important, because it gives cohesive strength to groups and reminds us that, through our beliefs, philosophy and practice of our daily lives, we ally and commit ourselves to a body of like-minded others.

Throughout this book we have been looking at universal features of human beings, and in particular the spaces that they require to feel safe and to flourish. Right at the start of the book we made some reference to something called mind space. That space was broadly concerned with the more subtle constructions that we placed upon our existence. At a more immediate level, it is concerned with our own personal direction and fulfilment, the things that we identify as meaningful to ourselves, the aspects of ourselves that we identify as uniquely personal. It is concerned with self-fulfilment, achievement, mastery and so forth. All this, however, can exist side by side with a much more pervasive aspect of belief which, in the broader sense, we may call wider belief and which most people identify as religion.

There can be no doubt that the capacity to believe in some higher ordering purpose and the personification of that in some higher being is a common attribute of human activity. Spiritual experience throughout the world shows many universal features, as does the experience of something which we may call a deity. States of meditation, trance, ecstasy and love occur with extraordinary similarity throughout a whole range of human societies.

It is not part of the purpose of this book to argue for or against the existence of something which we might call God. Nor is it to argue how such a God, or a transcendent force, might be pursued, appreciated or worshipped. Part of the purpose of this book, however, is to remind us that some sort of belief of this kind seems to be an important part of human existence and, in fact, of safe space. Invariably it is found that the possession of religious faith, the appreciation of some kind of higher purpose and the commitment to some sort of ideal beyond simple self-satisfaction and self-indulgence gives to those who believe a sense of security, a sense of commitment and a sense of strength, which is useful to them, particularly in times of trial and struggle. That is not to argue that we should hold beliefs in God or spiritual matters simply because they are convenient or because they serve a useful purpose for us. It is simply to underline the fact that this universal aspect of human nature seems to fit easily and helpfully into the general pattern of our lives.

Religion, the pursuit of spiritual experience and an appreciation of God, like other aspects of human acitivity, is greatly influenced by culture and it changes and develops as culture and human intellect change and develop. It is noteworthy that most of the religious faiths and practices currently pursued in the world evolved and developed between one and three thousand years ago. It seems that a less organised polytheism characterised hunter/gatherer societies and that a monotheistic and more abstract God emerges in agricultural communities. Society is now further changing from a predominantly small group agricultural society to, in many places, a predominantly urban society, and technology has, of course, revolutionised not only our intellectual activities but our day to day lives. It seems highly likely religions and spiritual activity will undergo further changes in the coming hundred years or so. The last thirty years in the West, and in some of the Pacific countries, have witnessed the emergence of a number of new spiritual beliefs and practices. Some of these have many of the same moral values and an unquestionable debt of commitment to older religious practices which have inspired them.

It would be hard to estimate what percentage of personal effort, wealth, time and commitment many of our ancestors gave to constructing beautiful things that celebrated some higher and mysterious aspect of ourselves, but whatever percentage it was it was certainly very great. The Blue Mosque in Istanbul, the Temple in Jerusalem, the Great Pyramids, the Acropolis, the great Temples at Benares, Chartres Cathedral, the still and silent places of Kyoto – all these holy places, although sometimes in part built by slaves under duress, invariably expressed the transcendent faith of the civilisations that built them. Their existence acted as a unifying focus for those who saw them, and they carried with them some sort of message of faith, some sort of morality and some sort of purpose. Many of them were literally safe spaces (sanctuaries) and at the same time perhaps reflected a feeling of inner safety experienced by those who prayed at them.

Religious beliefs and religious groupings transcend the simple material constrictions of space and time and link us not only with those who have gone before but with those who follow.[19] They allow us to identify ourselves with humanity as a flow across time, unconstrained by individual self-interest, and unaffected by individual birth, life and death. This commitment to an uninterrupted timeless humanity is one that seems to be very important and one that reminds us that we owe a debt to those who went before and an obligation to those who will follow. In its morality it enshrines the basic rights and needs of human beings and other creatures on the earth, and in doing this offers us guides and constraints that are all too often missing.

Many people are once again trying to identify some kind of spiritual spark in themselves. They are not deterred if this does not conform to the belief patterns that their parents or grandparents pursued before them. The capacity to have spiritual experience, like the capacity to love, is an almost universal human endowment and, if it is there, it may be more important now than it ever was. Perhaps as the God without seems less available, the God within will become more so. The silent music, peace and safety of religious experience can still be attained.

12

WOMEN AND MEN

Before written culture, most of what we learned came from the group in which we lived. Today, even with multi-media information saturation, there are important things that we can best learn from other people – especially in the area of sexual and social roles and personal conduct.

In rural communities before the Industrial Revolution, a growing boy would gradually become less involved with his mother and develop new associations with his father and the other local men. In becoming a man and being accepted, according to standardised criteria, as a man among other men he would achieve a new and stable social base. He would be 'a man' and feel 'safe' with other men. Similarly a girl would move away from childhood to the secrets and mysteries of adult women, and eventually be accepted by the local women as part of their group.

With the coming of the Industrial Revolution this natural growth and development within a small group became much more difficult. Factory life brought with it a new set of values and new peers. With schooling difficulties, unemployment and the breakdown of cohesive communities, this culture of the same sex grouping becomes difficult to find or, if available, all too often maladaptive and quite out of touch with the real world. This is an age which is specially interested in personal development and individuality seen at their extreme in the 'me generation'. This seems to have led to a certain isolation and a stange malaise of doubt and disillusionment. More and more of the goals and dreams that we set ourselves seem to be consumer fantasies which we cannot fulfil in the real world. Many teenagers seek to be 'film-stars' or 'athletes' or 'millionaires'. They have no real models for these ideals and no chance of achieving them. Lost in pursuit of unattainable fantasy, they feel isolated, alone and very unsafe. The reality of their progress and achievement in the world cannot be tested, is insubstantial and never good enough.

Society as a group of living, changing systems is flexible and adaptive. As some institutions decline and fall, new ones emerge to take their place. In the last twenty years few have made more impact on western society than the women's movement. This movement has not only provided new role models and new ideas of how women should live in society, but has also brought important sustaining on-going social support. Our study of safe spaces provided by our own sex would not be complete without a brief review of this. In the early groupings, inspired by a number of pioneering writers, a whole generation of women found, for the first time, a group of women where they could break silence.[1,2,3]

Lynda D., a marital therapist and counsellor, put it like this: 'For the first time I suddenly found somewhere where it seemed all right to say what I was really feeling . . . . The women seemed to be interested in what I was saying and were receptive. Together we seemed to develop our own new view of the world and that view was rather different from what we had been told we were supposed to feel.'

Elizabeth D., a successful dental specialist, describes her amazement at discovering 'that we all felt the same. For the first time I was able to share thoughts and feelings with other women. I discovered that in so many areas we were constrained by myths about how men and women ought to be and we have never looked at how they really were. Up until that time, although I hadn't realised it, I had been in competition with other women. For the first time I was able to free myself from this.'

Other women provided a safe space within which a supportive social system could develop. Some of this became formalised in a variety of co-counselling and self-help groups. One form of this is seen in consciousness-raising. In these groups, the women involved seek to redefine their problems and difficulties in terms of new and generally a feminist perspective.[4] One study found that women who had entered these groups showed more autonomy and assertiveness and became more interested in achievement and self-acceptance. Another detailed study of conscious-raising[5] looked at target problems and suggested that these tended to centre around concepts of self and problems of relations with other people. Problems with self included matters to do with self-esteem, assertion and identity, while relationship problems were related to marriage, family and relationships with other women. The most marked effect of consciousness-raising groups in this study was to increase self-esteem and self-reliance significantly, but more detailed changes in personal and other relationships were not always apparent. The authors go on to stress the value of these groups but suggest that they are not a substitute for psychotherapy or more intimate counselling in complex interpersonal issues.

Another study[6] looked at how these consciousness-raising groups could alter womens' response to widowhood. In this study there was a serious attempt to compare on a fairly scientific basis four different groups of women all of whom were attending some kind of therapeutic group. This study showed that the feminist-orientated consciousness-raising group was the most effective in producing positive changes.

One of the four As of course is assessment, and consciousness-raising for women contributes particularly to this aspect of their problem. Consider a woman whose space is unsafe – a woman living with a violent husband, living in a tower block, on social security. In response to the lack of safety in her life she begins to feel tense, worthless, helpless and hopeless. She respnds to these perhaps very natural feelings by wondering whether or not she is becoming ill or stupid or weak or ineffective. These inward-turning despairing analyses of the problem offer her nothing, and serve simply to reinforce her own feeling of uselessness and despair.

If we look again at her difficulties in the company of a women's group, in the presence of other women with similar problems, we can see at once that her feelings and unpleasant emotions may be nothing to do with illness, may be nothing to do with her being weak, or stupid, or failing, but may be a normal and understandable reaction to what is an intolerable environmental situation. Perhaps within such a group she may find other women with similar environments, with similar lack of safety, having similar feelings. This new assessment, with the possibility of mutual aid, can restore self-esteem, give hope and lead into positive action that often produces dramatic and useful changes.[6]

Most women are now freed from continuous child-bearing and many are being freed from economic dependence on men. The support role that women for so long provided is being questioned and modified.[7] The challenge for the future is to define a new feminine role and identity that is different from that of man, yet truly and honestly fulfilling to women.[8,9]

Whilst women have done a great deal to alter and change their behaviour and conditions, men seem to have made less progress in this direction and given the matter less attention. For this reason and because lack of safety and support seems to be a major problem for modern men, we shall look in a little more detail at the spaces that men create between them and the structures that flourish among them (and also at the structure in which men participate and the spaces that they create).

The study of higher animals, of other cultures and of our own folklore, shows that without doubt a major source of strength, aid, safety and support for men can derive from identity with a male group and mutual cooperation. In animals, male groups are often well organised with a leader and subordinate males. In some higher apes, many of the younger and less dominant males group together in 'bachelor bands' which exist outside the family group.

In many human societies the men often live together in special quarters and engage together in exclusively male activities which often involve hunting, offence and defence. Admission to these groups is carefully controlled and may involve initiation rites. These patterns have wide expression in our own culture. The old guilds and city companies had apprenticeship periods, and once these were completed the young man, often with much ceremony, would be admitted to the group. Once in the group, he was assured of certain rights and support from the group, and this would often extend into age and infirmity.

Over the last hundred years or so there has been no shortage of these male groupings. They may be seen everywhere, at the local pub, in the army, in football teams, big companies, certain trade unions, among freemasons and so on. For all that, some of them seem to have got themselves a bad reputation. The so-called 'football hooligans' offer an interesting paradigm. Here is a male grouping, that clearly derives its origins from deep-rooted male needs, but probably provides very little constant mutal support for those within the group, and to those outside presents only violence and brutality, male power without concern or morality. A proliferation of small self-interested groups within a society, whilst giving strength to their affiliates, can be very damaging to those who are identified as being 'out' of the group. Thus, the wrong kind of colours on a football scarf can lead to a savage attack, or even murder, even though the wearer may live in the same town as those who attacked him. Too many small self-interested groups, unrestrained by much morality, make society very unsafe and unstable.

Just as the football hooligan has to go on rampaging to maintain his place, so the 'executive' in the big multi-international has to parade his 'chargeable time sheet' and his profitability every month and stay ahead of his field, and if he does not deliver he is out. Testing is certainly a big part of male grouping, but constant testing associated with pervasive insecurity is clearly undesirable.

For many modern men, admission to some male groups ironically diminishes safe space and dramatically increases stress. The leader of the group, instead of showing concern for his group members, encourages intra-group rivalry in pursuit of his own self-advancement. To make it all more complex, he will constantly deny self-interest and, rather like so many politicians, endlessly proffer altruism and group welfare as his major concerns. This spirit runs all through many big organisations and takes its toll. Unfortunately, it also gets results, and it is results that the man at the top wants. The 'hungry' succeed and the others go under, shunted off to the periphery – to the psychiatrist or alcoholics anonymous. Anybody who dares to question the corporate ideal should clearly not be there, and will soon be out.

The group selects for ability, ambition, greed, envy, lack of principle and marginal dishonesty. These principles sometimes operate at the very highest levels of government, business and large organisations. Nobody cares – but everybody pretends to. Bonhomie and first names are de rigueur, but each smiling man (or woman) is looking over his shoulder for the knife that might replace the slap on the back.

We live in an age which seeks to play down our sexual differences. However, millions of years of evolution were directed at developing different roles for male and female. As outlined in an earlier chapter, hunting, defence of territory and attack in pursuit of new territory and other resources were the preserve of small groups of males.

For men, confrontation with danger and the expression of aggression, like most other human attributes, has become very much part of culture. Early cave paintings, dating back some thirty thousand years, have shown men pursuing animals. Long before these cave paintings, perhaps as long as six hundred thousand years ago, the Mindel glaciation yielded evidence that *homo erectus* hunted a variety of large animals that are now extinct, and smaller creatures such as zebras and pigs.

In our own culture those who can face loss of safety and stand up to danger and do well in the face of it are universally admired. They may be acclaimed as heroes, given public rewards such as medals or awards and quite often they may become 'rich and famous'. Many people, such as professional boxers and racing drivers, face danger in public, their performance under great stress being watched by millions of people. Rather as it was in the parable of the talents, so it might well be with safety and danger. Thus, the courage required by a partially sighted crippled old woman to cross roads and go shopping on her own might well be close to the courage displayed by a world champion boxer defending his title against a tough opponent. One kind of courage is public and makes a lot of noise, the other is silent and generally not noticed.

Myth and legend are full of archetypal descriptions of men and women in very unsafe situations facing up to them, and somehow overcoming them. We may face danger as part of challenge or test, or we may face it because we have to. In many societies, acceptance may involve some statutory confrontation with danger. Whatever the context, solid group support can aid and strengthen.

In a review of the British response to air raids, many authorities were surprised at the absence of large-scale panic among the British public, which was incidentally expected and prepared for. Although to some extent this may have been related to simply 'getting used' to them (habituation), an important part was played by group membership. As part of a group or team people had 'something to do'. Their task as warden or observer or whatever contributed to a feeling of mastery, of being able to do something about the problem. They also had responsibility for carrying others in the group who were distressed or afraid, an activity which in itself can help to reduce fear in the carrier. Thus the civil population under common threat created a mutually sustaining system in which each was able to support the other.[10]

Another wartime example was seen in air combat crews. Separation from the group in time of danger can produce very bad effects. These very brave men fought in the unsafest possible setting and had a short life expectancy. Yet morale was high and the men showed great courage. There seems little doubt that the ethos and spirit of the group contributed much to their ability to cope with the constant threat of injury or death.[10]

The emergence of the hero and his lore has occurred over the last three thousand years in a variety of cultures. 'Within increasing specialisation it becomes possible for small groups of an aristocratic warrior caste to dominate. Their adventures are extolled in poems and literature and their exploits are widely renowned. Fighting and adventure are their major interests and the common people are of little importance.'[11] The twelve labours of Hercules feature not only conflict with lions, hydra and wild boars, but a whole variety of additional exploits. Hercules eventually constructed his own funeral pyre and ascended to heaven to live happily ever after. Odin, the heroic Teutonic god, also known as Wodin, gave his name to Wednesday. He was involved in a variety of heroic exploits and later, as a god, granted heroism and literacy to mankind and decided man's fate. More recently we have had the Knights of the Round Table, the Sumarai of Japan, and a whole variety of other heroic men. Much of today's culture is still pre-occupied with the hero and many have gone as far as to suggest that at its peak the popularity of the president of the United States, Ronald Reagan, was related to his personification of the American heroic virtues portrayed on the screen by such actors as John Wayne.

Unfortunately, our world is getting rather too crowded for heroes, and the endless pursuit of heroic virtures. Within the tightly-knit urban societies in which most of us live, this is producing a whole variety of problems. These were described much earlier on in the chapter on cities and the problems of violence there. On a much larger scale, the hero armed with an atom bomb presents an unimaginably dangerous prospect. For, in pursuit of expression of heroic virtues and the fulfilment of cultural requirements, he may have to use that bomb and in its use may find some degree of self-fulfilment and self-realisation. At the same time, he will wipe out large sectors of humanity and possibly the whole of the world.

Unfortunately we do not live in an ideal world. Territory must be defended and those who are dependent, particularly children and older people, must be protected against attack and violence. Some kind of heroic class is still required and some kind of weaponry is also required. We are caught in the most dreadful dilemma. How are we to obtain safety for those we love and care about whilst, at the same time, not destroying the world? How are we to obtain a share of limited resources that we need for survival and normal life whilst, at the same time, ensuring that the pursuit of those resources does not destroy us? More and more people live on a planet that will not get any larger.

We have to face and deal with the problem of aggression and violence and competition for resources and safety. Exactly how we are going to do this remains entirely unclear, but it is important to pose the problem and to state its special relevance to men, for unfortunately it is men who have the greater genetic propensity to violence and it is in the hands of man that much of the technology of violence now rests.

Men have to find new ways. Just as women have grappled with the tyranny of reproduction and a five-thousand-year-old culture surrounding it, so men must face the tyranny of their aggression and competitiveness and the three thousand years of hero and warrior culture that goes with that.

Man's once adaptive biology has generated a culture which has had the effect of magnifying and extolling aggressive tendencies, as well as of making him face himself and other men over and over in absurdly vacuous competition. This, of course, is expressed not just in violence but in achievement, ostentation and material aggrandisement.

Lizzie D., who earlier in the chapter related her experience of feminism, said at one stage: 'I realised that I not only had an absurd idea of what men wanted from me, but an equally absurd idea of what I was supposed to expect from men.'

Could it be that enlightened women will help men to change? Another genetic male endowment, central to classic evolutionary theory, is competition for females – sexual selection. Once again culture moulds and shapes this basic propensity – if women were to look at what they really want from men, rather than what they were 'supposed' to want from men. If women were to start asking for, and responding positively to, an altered style, then men might start offering that altered style. Could it be that men are feeling not only unsafe, but lost and perplexed? Some of the women are in competition with them – some want more and more of what the old culture says they ought to want and the remainder don't care, or want nothing whatsoever to do with what they see as an outmoded and maladaptive male style.

The effort of trying to be too many things to too many people, and the effort of trying too hard,[12] is catching up with men, who are failing in the biggest epidemic of heart and circulatory disease ever seen.[13,14] Increasingly futile effort produces 'periods of rage, fear, furious struggling, alternating with periods of defeat, despair and wanting to give up.'[15] Emotion is denied and effort is increased in a setting of continuous arousal of both the adrenal fight and flight system and the stress adaptation system. The cardiovascular system suffers the major effect of this impossible effort and the result is heart disease and death.[12,17]

As described in the last chapter, a number of ingenious studies have shown that in a whole variety of unsafe situations, biochemical change within the body can be greatly reduced by effective social support. Rises in blood pressure, cholesterol and uric acid can all be diminished by the people around us. This is not just mind over body, it's other people over body.[18] These startling observations led a number of investigators to look more deeply at the body's response to the space in which it exists.

For a long time many researchers have been convinced that just as we have a bodily response to hostile space, we do actually have a positive bodily response to safe space. Just as we adapt to lack of safe space, so there seems to be an identifiable physiological response that occurs when we are warm, secure, safe and with those we love. We may call it the safe space response, although it has also been described as the housekeeping response or the relaxation response. It operates when we feel a sense of complete safety, both materially and personally, and especially when we are with a supportive group of friends or a particular person we love and trust.

The brain brings about this state by using a variety of mechanisms. Firstly it drastically diminishes the activity of the two unsafe space responses, the adrenalin alarm system and the steroid adaptation system, but it also makes use of two other mechanisms. The first is a part of the nervous system, called the parasympathetic, whose activities promote digestion, slow the heart beat, encourage sexual excitement and encourage other various consolidating bodily functions.

As well as that, the brain makes use of its own morphine-like substances – the endorphins – which suppress pain and produce feelings of calm and tranquility. The two opposing bodily modes – the safe and the unsafe (parasympathetic – calm and sympathetic – aroused) can easily be seen as expressions of the yin and yang of Chinese medicine. On the one hand affiliation, calm, conservation and consolidation (parasympathetic or yang) and on the other hand retaliation, fight and flight (sympathetic or yin).

The Chinese believed that the heart contained the mind (in fact the heart and mind are intimately connected through sympathetic and parasympathetic nerves, whose anatomy and function have been quite well defined) and that the spiritual soul was controlled by the liver. This control was mediated through the meridians which could be interfered with by using acupuncture needles. Acupuncture affects the brain function by bringing about the release of endorphins, the opiate-like substances naturally occurring in the brain, and through this and other mechanisms, not yet understood, it may affect disease processes and bodily function in general, perhaps by encouraging the safe space response.

Patients with cardiovascular disease show a decrease of these catabolic (body-building) parasympathetic processes (associated with a decrease in the production of insulin and testosterone) and they also show an overactivity of the sympathetic system. Their bodies are out of balance and eventually this imbalance can lead to heart disease and high blood pressure.

A variety of stresses and personality factors have been shown to contribute to this, but only very recently has it been realised that the safe space of love, intimacy and personal trust can, through the hormonal systems that we have just reviewed, not only protect against heart disease[19] but lessen many of the bodily effects of stress by lowering the blood pressure, slowing the heart and reducing the amount of cholesterol circulating.[18]

Thus safe space provided by living links protects us against stress, but it also has its own positive replenishing effects which actually help the body to function better. Rather as sleep is an essential part of our physiological balancing system, so the safe space response has health-giving effects we have ignored for too long.

With the world and social conditions that currently prevail, it is probably too early to expect the eclipse of Hercules and Odin, but perhaps the role models of Jesus and Buddha, available for so long, might at least begin to moderate and soften the one-sided caricature to which so many modern men aspire. Men need their instinctive roots and male energy, but that must not be a tyranny that enslaves them. Somehow men must find a new moderate balanced ideal of maleness – the archetypal strong male tempered by a wise, sensitive and moral side. Men must father their sons again and sons must find fathers – not just biological fathers, but older, wiser men they can trust and respect and learn from.

Men need not only a male ideal but the corporate strength and safety of a caring and supportive male grouping. Yet this must not involve just an endless commitment to strength and power, for this produces an unbalanced, over-developed caricature, blown up like the old iron-pumping body builder. The stereotyped male leader figure who is autonomous, independent and assertive has been taught to reject and deny his fragility and his needs for nurture and retreat. This often leads to a failure on his part to recognise his needs, his wholeness and humanity, which must include both weak and strong and a failure to satisfy those needs either in himself or his friends.

Men need their masculinity, but it must be tempered and moderated by intellect and morality. That morality, once derived from religion, must now stand on its own in the form of goodness and kindness and humanity – because they are right and because they are the only hope. Men also need femininity, not only within women but within themselves – the womanly side to men can greatly help to create the balance.

Somewhere there is goodness and safety and moderation in male groupings, but you have to look hard for it. Women have started to look for new ways, now it is the turn of the men. Some men are beginning to look for affection, assessment, affirmation and aid and some are beginning to find them.

CONCLUSION:
LIVING WITH REALITY

New insights about ourselves and our relationship with the world are so very important, for it is these that may help us to see ourselves and the world as they really are. Only then can we begin to make realistic changes in our families, our work, our health, our housing and our ambitions. Reality will encourage an adaptation that accepts and recognises our human nature and, at the same time, nature's nature.

Yet there is much more to life than just adaptation. We are creatures who love novelty, excitement, change, challenge, pleasure, fun and innovation. We can be aggressive, assertive, brave and courageous. Although we often pursue our own interests, all through history we have made the most amazing sacrifices for those whom we love and care about. We can symbolise and abstract and, in the world of encoded experience that spans time, we can, through books, paintings, magnetic tapes and laser discs, relate to the ideas and concepts of men and women long dead.

This survey of safe space does not seek to reduce us to termites or dung beetles or Kafka's man in his burrow. Fifteen thousand years ago we still had spare energy to decorate our caves. Even the poorest and most oppressed peoples of the world will try to find the energy to 'whoop' and dance and sing and make music. In terrible conditions of misfortune and deprivation, our individuality and our self-expression drive us to create, record, analyse, commuicate and survive.

We will take a large proportion of our wealth and our time and our energy to pursue the idea of a transcendent force or God, construct great monuments and temples, move great stones, heap up small mountains, and worship, sing, contemplate and meditate.

Safe space is not a manifesto for reductionism and despair. It does not offer a damaged, compromised retreating view of humanity. Quite the reverse. It accepts all our extraordinary potential but it seeks to place it in context.

It is people who create culture, but before that in order to live they require certain basic conditions. Their energies are naturally at first directed towards these and when they are, at least partially, attained, then they may go on to

159

pursue a whole lot of other extraordinary and often diverse activities.

Perhaps because the attainment of 'good enough' conditions is often difficult, most cultures have come to idealise physical strength and violence, for all too often we have had to compete with other creatures or with each other for resources – often in brutal and terrible ways.

Does the decline of the Mother Goddess as the dominant force and the emergence of the aggressive male warrior civilisations correlate with the rise in human population and an ensuing battle for resources?

As strength and power and aggression have been idealised, so perhaps we have progressively sought to deny our basic needs in pursuit of ideals of toughness, independence, aggression and defiance.

In many cultures, toughness and tenderness seem to have become mutually exclusive. To be strong became incompatible with having needs or admitting to them, so that some absurd parody of the male warrior has emerged, often with a very unpleasant set of morals and some very unpleasant behaviour to go with it. There have been many exceptions to this. For example, in Taoist teaching the strong and the weak (the yielding) were seen as closely interrelated virtues to be carefully cultivated. Similarly the Knights Templar sought to combine a code of chivalry, a strong faith and their own special and enduring ideals of romanticism.

It seems that for many reasons we now find ourselves in the midst of the biggest cover-up since the beginning of culture – a collective denial of who and what we really are, a denial that we feel pain when hurt, anguish when threatened with separation from those we love, and depression and grief when we lose (particularly in death) those for whom we care.

We all want to be strong and to see ourselves as strong and show defiance and fortitude and bravery, but there has never been a brave man or woman who did not bleed or hurt or grow old or die. And there have only been a few people who cared nothing for anyone else in the world, who did not need somebody. All this we obtain from the close and intimate links of love, of family and community. It is we alone who can create the system and the spaces for this. All this is part of our nature, our sensitivity, our frailty, that part which needs nurture, love and safety. It is all a central part of us.

Is that admission so terrible, is that aspect of our own nature so threatening that we must deny it and abuse it? We are not the first to have done this. The Spartans left their children out in the cold to perish. The ascetics of many religions have sought to deny parts of their humanity in the name of God. For them it was temptation, sin or distraction, but perhaps deep down it was frailty, it was their inescapable humanity that in the final analysis they could not stand. Saint Augustine's *Confessions* suggest he was puzzled, almost bewildered, by his body's annoying tendency to feel desire. No doubt, at an intellectual level it was the immorality of all this that troubled him, but could it have been that deep down it was the final symbol of his humanity that he could not escape –

built into his very being as a biological legacy of millions of years of evolution? He could not avoid the social and sexual power of other human beings. No wonder others tried to mutilate their genitals to rid themselves of any physical expression of their love and their neediness.

We can't go on pretending to be what we want to be or what others expect us to be. We must stop for just a moment and ask what we are really like. If we can begin to get an answer to that and then we can begin to get an answer to what the other person is really like, perhaps then we will find a better basis for interrelating and perhaps the world will have a better chance.

Of course, it might be that we would find our own true nature to be cruel and amoral and beyond hope, some dark vision of original sin with little prospect of any better version of human nature ever emerging. Much of nature seems to be against this – there is still good cause for hope. Looking at what is wrong with the world is not meant to be simple self-flagellation, nor is it an exercise in self-indulgent despair. It is an attempt to look at what is wrong in the hope that, by understanding better what is wrong, we can start to put it right.

The timeless balance between adventure and security, danger and safety, activity and rest, is slowly but surely becoming unbalanced. In pursuit of more and more exciting space we are denying those things that are essential to our physical and psychological well-being, those things that are essential for regeneration and repair. We are becoming trees without roots, fish without water.

Here is the truth we would rather forget. Here, if anywhere, there is nemesis. Here, in defying our own nature and ignoring our own limits, we will eventually have to pay a price. Yet there are few dissenters or protesters. Why? Why does nobody say this is not the way we are?

Because now most of us are collaborators. This, in the psychoanalytic sense, is 'denial' as a defence. We choose not to see something because it is painful to us. It reminds us of an aspect of ourselves we would rather not recognise.

Safe space is very real. It is increasingly under threat and its preservation and creation becomes the responsibility of each and every one of us. We must create it – not only for ourselves but for those around us. Much of it exists between two people. It is something they create between themselves, which they can experience and which those close to them can experience. Much of it depends on consideration, concern, trust and love. We can create it first and foremost in our own lives, in our own families and our places of work. We retain much responsibility for the spaces immediately around us. Let us remember that safe space is precious and important, we all need it and we can't live without it.

On a larger scale safe space does involve material conditions – the kinds of rooms and homes and cities in which we live, and beyond that, the world in which we live, the air we breathe, the water we drink, the food we eat.

Safeguarding all of this must become a high priority for each and every one of us and we must pursue it through pressure groups and through existing political machinery.

Yet all this striving, which is so very necessary and so very important, will come to nothing if we fail in the final analysis to grasp that no matter how balanced and safe the world might become it will stand for nothing if we cannot be at ease with it, satisfied with it, and feel safe with it. Balance and safety without must find their counterpart in balance and safety within. The God without must come alive as the God within. The struggle – so often an end – must have an end. There are questions we cannot answer, desires we cannot satisfy. The realisation and definition of safety within ourselves and with ourselves is perhaps the most difficult challenge of it all. Yet if each of us could sit in silence for one minute or even one second each day and feel truly safe, then we would be well on the way.

At times it seems as if we are forgetting what every previous generation knew. Let us try to remember before it is too late. If we do not reverse current trends, safe space at all levels will become increasingly hard to find. Our good sense is not going to fail us at this critical point in history.

REFERENCES

CHAPTER 2: CRISIS AND CHALLENGE

1 Palling, B. (1986) India defends its two billion pound claim for Bhopal victims. *The Independent*, 24 November
2 Gleser, G.C. *et al.* (1981) A Study of Buffalo Creek. New York: Academic Press
3 Lannoy, R. (1971) The Speaking Tree. Oxford: OUP
4 Rosen, G. (1975) Nostalgia: a 'forgotten' psychological disorder. *Psychological Medicine* 5(4),340-354
5 Sargent, W. (1967) The Unquiet Mind. London: Heinemann
6 Dohrenwend, B.S. *and* Dohrenwend, B.P. *eds.* (1974) Stressful Life Events: Their Nature and Effects. Chichester: Wiley
7 Parkes, C. Murray- *and* Brown, R. (1972) Health after bereavement: a controlled study of young Boston widows and widowers. *Psychosomatic Medicine* 34,449-461
8 Parkes, C.Murray- (1972) Bereavement: Studies in Grief in Adult Life. London: Tavistock
9 Parkes, C. Murray- *et al.* (1969) Broken heart: a statistical study of increased mortality among widowers. *British Medical Journal* 1,740-743
10 Rees, W.D. *and* Lutkins, S.G. (1969) Morality and bereavement. *British Medical Journal* 4,13
11 Parkes, C. Murray- (1971) The first year of bereavement: a longitudinal study of the reaction of widows to the death of their husbands. *Psychiatry* 33,444
12 Rahe, R.H. (1968) Life-change measurement as a predictor of illness. *Proceedings of the Royal Society of Medicine* 61,1124-1126
13 Miller, F.T. *et al.* (1974) Perception of life crisis events. *In* Stressful Life Events: Their Nature and Effects, edited by B.S. Dohrenwend and B.P.Dohrenwend. Chichester: Wiley
14 Solomon, G.F. (1985) The emerging field of psychoneuroimmunology. *Advances* 2(1),6-19
15 Brown, G.W. *and* Birley, J.L.T. (1968) Crises and life changes and the onset of schizophrenia. *Journal of Health and Social Behavior* 9,203-214
16 Paykel, E.S. *et al.* (1975) Suicide attempts and recent life events. *Archives of General Psychiatry* 32,327-333
17 Myers, J.K. *et al.* Life events and psychiatric impairment. *Journal of Nervous and Mental Disease* 152,149-157
Brown, G.W. *and* Harris, T.O. (1978) Social Origins of Depression. London: Tavistock.

CHAPTER 3: US IN OUR WORLD

1 Dubois, R. (1980) Man Adapting. New Haven, Conn: Yale Univ. Press
2 Hecker, L.F.K. (1959) The Epidemics of the Middle Ages. London: Sydenham Society
3 Walsh, J.J. (1920) Medieval Medicine. London: Blackwell
4 Marti-Ibanez, F. (1962) A Pictorial History of Modern Medicine. London: Spring Books
5 Department of Health and Social Security (1986) AIDS Book 1: General Information for Doctors. Book 2: Information for Doctors Concerning the Introduction of the HTLV III Antibody Test. Heydon, Lancs: DHSS
6 Gillie, O (1986) Tenth of Ugandan adults infected. *The Independent* 4 December
7 Prentice, T. (1986) Aids: a world with no hiding place. *The Times* 19 November
8 Department of Health and Social Security (1980) Inequalities in Health. Report of a Research Working Group (Chairman: Sir Douglas Black). London: DHSS
9 Friends of the Earth Trust (1986) Acid Rain. London: The Trust
10 Katz, M. (1961) Some aspects of the physical and chemical nature of air pollution. *In* Air Pollution. pages 97-158. Geneva: World Health Organization (*Monograph series no.46*)
11 New Larousse Encyclopedia of Mythology (1968) London: Hamlyn
12 Gradusek, D.C. *and* Zigas, V. (1957) Degenerative disease of the central nervous system in New Guinea: the endemic occurrence of 'kuru' in the native population. *New England Journal of Medicine* 257,874
13 Moriyama, I.M. *and* Kato, H. (1973) Mortality Experience of A-bomb Survivors 1970-1972. Atomic Bomb Commission (*Technical Reports* 15-73)
14 Jacobi, W. (1976) Interpretation of measurements in uranium mines, dose evaluation and biomedical aspects. *In* Proceedings of Specialist Meetings on Personal Dosimetry and Area Monitoring Suitable for Radon Daughter Products, Elliot Lake, Canada, October 1976. Pages 33-48. Paris: OECD/NEA
15 Modan, B.*et al.* (1974) Radiation induced head and neck tumours. Lancet 1,277
16 Brown, P. (1986) New Dounreay Survey link with child cancers. *Guardian* 10 June
17 Ivens, M.(1986) Chernobyl cancer will kill 48,000. *Daily Telegraph* 26 August
18 Wilson, W. (1986) How the cover was blown. *The Observer* 11 May
19 Patterson, Walter C. (1976) Nuclear Power. Harmondsworth: Pelican Books
20 Capra, F. (1983) The Turning Point. London: Fontana
21 Howe, George Melvyn (1980) Environmental Medicine. 2nd ed. London: Heinemann
22 Vulliamy, W. (1986) Drillers getting through, say villagers. *Guardian* 30 August
23 Bellini, J. (1986) High Tech Holocaust. Newton Abbot: David & Charles
24 Wilson, E.O. (1980) Sociobiology. Cambridge, Mass: Harvard Univ.Press
25 The I Ching or Book of Changes (1965) The Richard Wilhelm Translations, translated by C.F. Baynes. London: Routledge and Kegan Paul

CHAPTER 4: SAFE SPACE AND LIVING SYSTEMS

1 Illich, I. (1977) Limits to Medicine: Medical Nemesis, the Expropriation of Health. Harmondsworth: Penguin Books

2 Capra, F. (1986) Wholeness and health. *Holistic Medicine* 1(2) 145-159
3 Jantsh, E. (1967) Technological Forecasting in Perspective. Paris: OECD
4 Engel, G.L. (1980) The clinical application of the biopsychosocial model. *American Journal of Psychiatry* 137(5),535-544
5 Maslow, A. (1971) The Farther Reaches of Human Nature. Harmondsworth: Penguin Books
6 Hunt, John W. (1986) London Business School- Personal communication. (The author is grateful to Professor Hunt for permission to quote some of his lecture notes and also extremely grateful for a long discussion that has helped greatly in the formulation of the author's ideas)
7 Shah, Idries (1964) The Sufies. London: Cape
8 Engel, G.L. (1977) The need for a new medical model: a challenge for bio-medicine. *Science* 196,42-86

CHAPTER 5: ALL SYSTEMS GO

1 Kidel, M *and* Rowe-Leet (1986) Mapping the Body. Exhibition at London Ecology Centre
2 McClean, P. (1962) New findings relevant to the evolution of psychosexual functions of the brain. *Journal of Nervous and Mental Disease* 135(4)
3 McClean, P. (1964) Man and his animal brain. *Modern Medicine* 95-106
4 Luria, A.R. (1973) The Working Brain: an Introduction to Neuropsychology. Harmondsworth: Penguin Books
5 Hampshire, Stuart (1972) Freedom of Mind. Oxford: Clarendon Press
6 Levine, S. (1985) A definition of stress. *In* Animal Stress, edited by C.P. Moberg. Bethesda, Md: American Physiological Society
7 Seyle, H. (1974) Stress without Distress. London: Hodder & Stoughton
8 Henry, J.P. (1985) Neuroendocrine patterns of emotional response. *In* Emotion, Theory, Research and Experience. Vol.3, edited by R. Puluchick and H. Kellerman. New York: Academic Press
9 Vilensky, J.A. *et al.* (1982) The limbic system in human evolution. *Journal of Human Evolution* 11,447
10 Rachman, S.J. (1978) Fear and Courage. San Francisco: W.H. Freeman
11 Lang, P. *et al.* (1970) A psychophysiological analysis to fear modification using an automated desensitisation technique. *Journal of Abnormal Psychology* 76,220-234
12 Health and Personal Social Services Statistics for England 1982. London: HMSO
13 Annual Abstract of Statistics 1985. London: HMSO

CHAPTER 6: SURVIVING IN THE CITY

1 Maxwell, M.(1986) Human Evolution: a Philosophical Anthropology. Beckenham: Croom Helm
2 Clarke, G. (1969) World Prehistory: a New Outline. Cambridge: CUP
3 Thomas, H. (1979) Unfinished History of the World. London: Hamish Hamilton
4 Van der Post, L. (1958) The Lost World of the Kalahari. Harmondsworth: Penguin Books

5 Rocha, J. (1986) Brazilian police use murder to fight crime wave. *Guardian* 20 August

6 Howe, George Melvyn (1980) The environment, its influences and hazards to health. *In* Environmental Medicine, edited by George Melvyn Howe. 2nd ed. London: Heinemann

7 Responses à la Violence (1977) Rapport du Comité Nationale de Prevention de la Violence. Paris: Presses Puchek

8 Wedmore, K.K. *and* Freeman, H.L. (1984) Social pathology and urban overgrowth. *In* Mental Health and the Environment, edited by H.L. Freeman. Edinburgh: Churchill Livingstone

9 Bagley, C. (1984) Urban delinquency: ecological and educational perspectives. *In* Mental Health and the Environment, edited by H.L. Freeman. Edinburgh: Churchill Livingstone

10 Cannon, C. (1984) Schools of delinquency.

11 Freeman, H.L. *ed.* (1984) Mental Health and the Environment. Edinburgh: Churchill Livingstone

12 Harrison, P. (1983) Inside the Inner City: Life under the Cutting Edge. Harmondsworth: Penguin Books

13 Kellet, J.M. (1984) Crowding and territory: a psychiatric view. *In* Mental Health and the Environment, edited by H.L. Freeman. Edinburgh: Churchill Livingstone

14 Prentice, T. (1986) Widening health gap between the rich and poor. *The Times* 4 September

15 Smith, R. (1986) [Series of articles on unemployment]. *British Medical Journal* **291**, 1024,1107,1191,1263,1338,1409,1492,1563,1626,1707 *and* **292**,263,320,400,470

16 Faris, R.E.L. *and* Dunham, W.H. (1960) Mental Disorders in Urban Areas: an Ecological Study of Schizophrenia and Other Psychoses. New York: Hafner

17 Timms, P. Fry, A.H. *and* Watson, J.P. Morbidity in the homeless and rootless. In preparation

18 Jones, K. (1982) Scull's dilemma. *British Journal of Psychiatry* **141**, 221-226

19 Scheflen, L.E. (1986) Human Territory. Englewood Cliffs, NJ: Prentice-Hall

20 Tinbergen, N. (1939) Field observations of East Greenland birds 2: the behavior of the snow bunting in Spring. *Transactions of the Linnaean Society, New York* **5**, 1-94

21 Somer, R. (1969) Personal Space. Englewood Cliffs, NJ: Prentice-Hall

22 Horowitz, M.J. *et al.* (1964) Body-buffer zone. *Archives of General Psychiatry* **11**,651-656

23 Conder, P.J. (1949) Individual distance *Ibis* **91**(4)

24 Schutz, W.C. (1958) A Three-Dimensional Theory of Interpersonal Behavior. New York: Holt, Rinehart and Winston

25 Colby, P. (1973) Effects of density, activity and personality on environment. *Journal of Research in Personality* **7**,45-80

26 Newman, O. (1972) Defensible Space. New York: Macmillan

27 Gillis, A.R. (1977) High rise housing and psychological strain. *Journal of Health and Social Behavior* **18**, 418-431

28 Gannay, D.R. (1981) Mental health and high flats. *Journal of Chronic Diseases* **34**, 431-432

29 Stewart, W.F.R. (1970) Children in Flats: a Family Study. London: NSPCC

30 Rainwater, L. (1966) Fear and the house as a haven in the lower class. *Journal of the American Institute of Planners* **32**, 23-37
31 Wing, J.K. *and* Brown, G.W. (1970) Institutionalism and Schizophrenia. Cambridge: CUP
32 Milne, A.A. (1927) Now we are Six. London: Methuen
33 Proust, M. (1960) Remembrance of Things Past. Trans. by C.K. Scott Moncrieff. London: Chatto & Windus
34 Painter, G. (1971) Marcel Proust: a Biography. Vols 1 and 2. London: Chatto & Windus
35 Langebach, R. (1984) Continuity and sense of place: the importance of the symbolic image. *In* Mental Health and the Environment, edited by H.L. Freeman. Edinburgh: Churchill Livingstone
36 Schumacher, E.F. (1974) Small is Beautiful. Tunbridge Wells: Abacus
37 Hall, R.E. (1985) Ask any Woman: a London Enquiry into Rape and Sexual Assault. Bristol: Falling Wall Press
38 Ginsberg, A. (1956) Howl and Other Poems. San Francisco: City Light Books (*Pocket Poet series no. 4*)
39 Clark, R. (1979) World Jujitsu Federation Programme. Master Media
40 Burroughs, W. (1964) The Naked Lunch. London: Calder
41 La Tzu (1963) Tao Te Ching. Trans. by D.C. Lau. Harmondsworth: Penguin Books
42 Maynard Smith, J. (1974) The theory of games and the evolution of animal conflicts. *Journal of Theoretical Biology* **47**, 209-211

CHAPTER 7: THE CHILD IN ALL OF US

1 Neumann, E. (1972) The Great Mother. Lawrenceville, NJ: Princeton Univ. Press (*Bolligen series, xlviii*)
2 De Rougement, D. (1956) Passion and Society. London: Faber
3 Klein, M. (1957) Envy and Gratitude. London: Tavistock
4 Winnicott, D.W. (1968) The Maturational Process and the Facilitating Environment: Infant Development. London: Hogarth
5 Morris, D. (1979) Intimate Behaviour. London: Triad
6 Schafer, R. (1983) The Analytic Attitude. London: Hogarth
7 Goodall, J. (1965) Chimpanzees of the Goube Stream Reserve. *In* Primate Behavior, edited by I. de Vere. New York: Holt, Rinehart and Winston
8 Bowlby, J. (1969) Attachment and Loss. Volume 1: Attachment. Harmondsworth: Penguin Books
9 Weiss, R.S. Attachment in adult life. *In* The Place of Attachment in Human Behaviour, edited by C. Murray-Parkes and J. Stevenson-Hinde. London: Tavistock
10 Salk, L. (1966) Thoughts on the concepts of imprinting and its place in early human development. *Canadian Psychiatric Journal* **2**, 295-305
11 Lorenz, K. (1937) The companion in the bird's world. *Auk* **54**, 247-273
12 Harlow, H.F. *and* Zinnerman, R.R. (1959) Affectional response in the infant monkey. *Science* **130**, 421-432

13 Morris, D. (1968) The Naked Ape. page 96. London: Corgi
14 Nabokov, V. (1955) Lolita. London: Corgi
15 Proust, M. (1913) Swann's Way. Trans. by K.C. Scott Moncrieff. pages 53-54. Harmondsworth: Penguin Books
16 Segal, R. (1975) Psychoanalytical approach to the treatment of schizophrenia. *In* Studies of Schizophrenia, edited by M. Lader. Headley, Ashford, Kent, for the World Psychiatric Association and the Royal College of Physicians
17 Freud, S. (1927) The Ego and the Id. London: Hogarth
18 Freud, S. (1962) Three Essays on the Theory of Sexuality. London: Hogarth.
19 Freud, A. (1937) The Ego and the Mechanisms of Defence. London: Hogarth
20 Segal, H. (1973) Introduction to the Work of Melanie Klein. London: Hogarth

CHAPTER 8: SAFETY IN LOVE

1 Andreas, *Capellanus* (1941) The Art of Courtly Love. Trans. by John J. Perry. New York: Columbia Univ. Press
2 De Rougement, D. (1956) Passion and Society. London: Faber
3 Weiss, R.S. (1982) Attachment in adult life. *In* The Place of Attachment in Human Behaviour, edited by C. Murray-Parkes and J. Stevenson-Hinde. London: Tavistock
4 Lewis, C.S. (1960) The Four Loves. London: Bles
5 May, R. (1969) Love and Will. London: Fontana
6 Guenther, H.V. (1976) The Tantric View of Life. Boulder, Colorado: Shambhala (distributed by Routledge and Kegan Paul)
7 Skynner, A.C.R. (1976) One Flesh, Separate Persons. London: Constable
8 Morris, D. (1979) Intimate Behaviour. London: Triad
9 Breen, D. (1975) The Birth of a First Child: Towards an Understanding of Femininity. London: Tavistock
10 Thomas, P.D. *et al.* (1985) Effect of social support on stress-related changes in cholesterol level, uric acid level, and immune function in an elderly sample. *American Journal of Psychiatry* 142, 735-737
11 Hemingway, E. (1956) The Happy Life of Francis Macomber. *In* The First Forty-Nine Stories. London: Cape
12 Stoller, R.J. (1969) Sex and Gender. London: Hogarth
13 Dicks, H.V. (1967) Marital Tensions. London: Routledge and Kegan Paul
14 Main, T.F. (1966) Mutual projection in a marriage. *Comprehensive Psychiatry* 7, 432
15 Claremont de Castillejo, I. (1974) Knowing Woman. New York: Harper & Row
16 Lannoy, R. (1971) The Speaking Tree: a Study of Indian Culture and Society. Oxford: OUP
17 De Smedt, M. (1981) Chinese Eroticism. London: Miller
18 Dickson, S. (1985) The Mirror Within. London: Quartet
19 Smart, E. (1966) By Grand Central Station I Sat Down and Wept. London: Panther Books
20 Dames, M. (1976) The Great Goddess Rediscovered: the Silbury Treasure. London: Thames and Hudson

21 Neumann, E. (1972) The Great Mother. Lawrenceville, NJ: Princeton Univ.Press (*Bollingen series xlviii*)
22 Masters, W. and Johnson, V. (1970) Human Sexual Inadequacy. Boston, Mass: Little, Brown
23 Gillie, O. (1986) Tenth of Ugandan adults infected. *The Independent* 4 December
24 Prentice, T. (1986) Aids: a world with no hiding place. *The Times* 19 November
25 Porter, Roy (1986) History says no to the policeman's response to Aids. *British Medical Journal* 293, 1589
26 Massam, A. (1986) Death of a continent: African Aids threat. *The London Standard* 25 November
27 Verlaine, P. (1979) Femmes Hombres. Trans. by A. Elliot, London: Anvil Press Poetry
28 Department of Health and Social Security (1986) AIDS Book 1: General Information for Doctors. Heydon, Lancs: DHSS
29 Department of Health and Social Security (1986) AIDS Book 2: Information for Doctors Concerning the Introduction of the HTLV III Antibody Test. Heydon, Lancs: DHSS
30 Bynum, W.F. (1986) Threatening the wages of sin. *In* Medical Fringe and Medical Orthodoxy, 1750-1850, edited by W.F. Bynum and R. Port. Beckenham, Croom Helm
31 Boswell, J. (1982) Boswell's London Journal, 1762-1763. Edited by F.A. Pottle. London: Futura
32 Parkes, C. Murray- (1972) Bereavement: Studies of Grief in Adult Life. London: Tavistock
33 Medalie, J.H. and Goldbourt, U. (1976) Angina pectoris among 10,000 men. *American Journal of Medicine* 60(6), 910-921
34 Brown, G.W. and Harris, T.O. (1978) Social Origins of Depression. London: Tavistock
35 Baudelaire, C. (1955) The Flowers of Evil. Edited by M. Matthews and J. Matthews. New York: New Directions
36 Hemingway, E. (1956) The First Forty-Nine Stories. London: Cape
37 Timmins, N. (1986) Divorce figures show sharp rise. *The Independent* 26 November
38 Argyll, M. and Henderson, M. (1986) The Anatomy of Relationships. Harmondsworth: Penguin Books

CHAPTER 9: FINDING SAFETY AND CLOSENESS

1 Skynner, R. and Cleese, J. (1983) Families and How to Survive Them. London: Methuen
2 Frank, J.D. (1963) Persuasion and Healing. New York: Schocken Books
3 Freud, S. (1926) Inhibitions, Symptoms and Anxiety. Standard edition vol.20, pages 7-175. London: Hogarth (1959)
4 Fry, A. (1973) The concept of the unconscious. Paper presented at the Catholic University, Rome
5 Fairbairn, W. and Ronald, D. (1955) Observations in defence of the object relations theory of the personality. *British Journal of Medical Psychology* 28, 156

6 Schafer, R. (1983) The Analytic Attitude. London: Hogarth *and* Institute of Psychoanalysts

7 Frank, J.D. (1974) Therapeutic components of psychotherapy: a 25-year progress report on research. *Journal of Nervous Diseases* 159, 325-342

8 Malan, D.H. (1963) A Study of Brief Psychotherapy. London: Tavistock

9 Greenson, R. (1967) The Technique and Practice of Psychoanalysis. vol.1. Madison, Conn: International Universities Press

10 Rogers, C.R. (1951) Client Centered Therapy: its Current Practice, Implications and Theory. Boston, Mass: Houghton Mifflin

11 Truax, C.B. and Carkhuff, R.R. (1967) Toward Effective Counselling and Psychotherapy: Training and Practice. Chicago: Aldine

12 Malan, D.H. (1979) Individual Psychotherapy and the Science of Psychodynamics. London: Butterworths

13 McGuire, W. *ed.* (1974) The Freud/Jung Letters. Trans. by R. Mankin and R.F.C. Hull. London: Hogarth *and* Routledge and Kegan Paul

CHAPTER 10: ILLNESS AND VULNERABILITY

1 Tahka, V. (1984) The Patient Doctor Relationship. Baltimore, Md: Williams & Wilkins

2 Chrisman, N. (1977) The health seeking process: an approach to the natural history of illness. *Culture, Medicine and Psychiatry* 1(4), 351-377

3 Department of Health and Social Security (1980) Inequalities in Health. Report of a Research Working Group (Chairman: Sir Douglas Black). London: DHSS

4 Kidel, M. (1986) The meaning of illness. *Holistic Medicine* 1(1), 15-26

5 Zeigler, A. (1986) Personal communication (Dartington Conference)

6 Hellman, C. (1981) 'Tonic', 'fuel' and 'food': social and symbolic aspects of the long term use of psychotropic drugs. *Social Science and Medicine* 15b(4), 521-534

7 Fitzpatrick, R. (1984) Lay concepts of illness. *In* The Experience of Illness, edited by R. Fitzpatrick *et al*. London: Tavistock

8 Bradley, N.C.A. (1981) Expectation and experience of people who consult in a training practice. *Journal of the Royal College of General Practitioners* 31(28), 420-425

9 Illich, I. (1977) Limits to Medicine: Medical Nemesis, the Expropriation of Health. Harmondsworth: Penguin Books

10 Fry, A.H. (1986) Coming of age. *Holistic Medicine* 1(1), 1

11 Eisenberg, L. (1977) Disease and illness: distinctions between professional and popular ideas of sickness. *Culture, Medicine and Psychiatry* 1(1), 9-23

12 Balint, M. and Balint, E. (1961) Psychotherapeutic Techniques in Medicine. London: Tavistock

13 Fry, A.H. (1975) Explanations and understanding in general psychiatry: two fundamental approaches of the treatment and approach to the patient. *British Journal of Medical Psychology* 48(1), 77-83

14 DiMatteo, M.R. *et al.* (1980) Predicting patient satisfaction from physicians' non-verbal communication skills. *Medical Care* 18(4), 376-387

15 Egbert, L.D. and Egbert, A.L. (1964) Reduction of post operative pain by encouragement and instruction of patients. *New England Journal of Medicine* 270, 825

16 Clement-Jones, V. (1985) Cancer and beyond: the formation of BACUP. *British Medical Journal* **291**, 1021

CHAPTER 11: LIVING LINKS

1 House, J.S. (1981) Work Stress and Social Support. 2: The Nature of Social Support. Reading, Mass: Addison-Wesley
2 Huntingford, F. (1984) The Study of Animal Behaviour. London: Chapman and Hall
3 Argyll, M. *and* Henderson, M. (1986) The Anatomy of Relationships. Harmondsworth: Penguin Books
4 Kahn, R.L. and Antonucci, R.C. (1980) Convoys over the life course, attachment, roles and social support. *In* Life Span, Development and Behavior. Vol.3, edited by P.B. Batts and O.G. Brin. New York: Academic Press
5 Veitch, A. (1985) Unemployment adds to doctors' caseloads. *Guardian* 8 November
6 Warr, P. (1983) Work, jobs and unemployment. *Bulletin of the British Psychological Society* **36**, 305-311
7 Nathanson, C.A. (1980) Social roles and health status among women: the significance of employment. *Social Science and Medicine* **14a**, 463-471
Warr, P. *and* Parry, G. (1982) Paid employment and women's psychological well-being. *Psychological Bulletin* **91**, 475-516
8 Wheeler, L. *et al.* (1983) Loneliness, social interaction and social roles. *Journal of Personality and Social Psychology* **45**, 943-953
9 Sassoon, S. (1975) The Complete Memoirs of George Sherston. London: Faber
10 Neighbours and Loneliness (1982) London: Market Opinion and Research Institute (MORI)
11 Chambers, W.N. *and* Reser, H.F. (1953) Loss of safety triggering disease: congestive heart failure. *Psychosomatic Medicine* **15**, 39-60
12 Cobb, S. (1974) Physiological changes in men whose jobs were abolished. *Journal of Psychosomatic Research.* **18**, 245-258
13 Murphy, E. (1982) Social Origins of Depression in Old Age. *British Journal of Psychiatry* **141**, 135-142
14 Murgatroid, S. *and* Woolfe, R. (1982) Coping with Crisis: Understanding and Helping People in Need. London: Harper and Row
15 Henry, J.P. *and* Cassell, J.C. (1969) Psychosocial factors in essential hypertension: recent epidemiological and animal experimental evidence. *American Journal of Epidemiology* **90**, 171-200
16 Lieberman, M.A. *et al.* (1981) The psychotherapeutic impact of women's consciousness-raising groups. *In* Women and Mental Health, edited by E. Howell and M. Bayes. New York: Basic Books (distributed by Harper & Row)
17 Vaux, R. de (1961) Ancient Israel. Chapter 1: Semitic sanctuaries. London: Darton, Longman & Todd
18 Johnston, W. (1976) Silent Mystic: the Science of Meditation. London: Fontana
19 Suzuki, S. (1970) Zen Mind, Beginner's Mind: Informal Talks on Zen Meditation and Practice. New York: Weatherhill

CHAPTER 12: WOMEN AND MEN

1 Greer, G. (1970) The Female Eunuch. New York: McGraw-Hill
2 Millett, K. (1970) Sexual Politics. New York: Doubleday
3 Friedan, B. (1963) The Feminine Mystique. New York: Del
4 Broverman, I.K. *et al.* (1970) Sex-role stereotypes and clinical judgements of mental health. *Journal of Consulting Psychology* 34, 1-7
5 Newton, E. *and* Walton, S. (1971) The personal is political: consciousness-raising and personal change in women's liberation movement. *In* Anthropologists Look at the Study of Women. Symposium presented at the American Anthropological Association, 19 November 1981. (Chairman: B.G. Schoepf)
6 Howell, E. *and* Bayes, M. (1981) Women and Mental Health. New York: Basic Books (distributed by Harper & Row)
7 Breen, D. (1975) The Birth of a First Child: Towards an Understanding of Femininity. London: Tavistock
8 Steinmann, A. (1974) Cultural values, female role expectancies and therapeutic goals. *In* Women in Therapy, edited by V. Franks and V. Burtle. New York: Brunner/Mazel
9 Keller, S. The female role: constants and change. *In* Women in Therapy, edited by V. Franks and V. Burtle. New York: Brunner/Mazel
10 Rachman, J. (1978) Fear and Courage.
11 Jackson, K.H. (1971) A Celtic Miscellany. Harmondsworth: Penguin Books
12 Nixon, P.G.F. (1976) The human function curve. *Practitioner* 217, 765-769; 935-944
13 Henry, P.J. and Stephens, P.M. (1977) Stress, Health and the Social Environment. New York: Springer-Verlag
14 Kagan, A. (1982) Introduction to the role of psychological stressors in ischaemic heart disease. *In* Psychological Problems Before and After Myocardial Infarction, edited by J.J. Kellerman. Basel: Karger
15 Engel, G.L. (1974) Memorial lecture. The psychosomatic approach to individual susceptibility to disease. *Gastroenterology* 67, 1085-1093
16 Taylor, G.J. (1986) Alexithymia: concept, measurement and implications for treatment. *American Journal of Psychiatry* 143, 725
17 Lawn, B. (1982) Mental stress, arrhythmias and sudden death. *American Journal of Psychology* 72, 177; 180
18 Thomas, P.D. *et al.* (1985) Effect of social support on stress-related changes in cholesterol level, uric acid level, and immune function in an elderly sample. *American Journal of Psychiatry* 142, 735-737
19 Medalie, J.H. *and* Goldbourt, H. (1976) Angina pectoris among 10,000 men. 2: psychosociate and other risk factors as evidenced by a multivariate analysis of a five year incident study. *American Journal of Medicine* 60(6), 910-921

INDEX